THE BOYS
FROM THE
BUSHES

Publication made possible by:

Jan M. Merrifield Fiedler   Edwin & Starlyn Hinkle   Martha Grubb

Randy & Eldonna Magnus   Floyd M. Pugh

Robert & Darlene Anderson	Kaci Epperson	Mary Lilly	Bill Bob Nix
Donald N. Armstrong	Connor Epperson	William Link	Frosty & Fay Nix
Susie Bader	Gerald D Fiedler	Betty L. Love	Lana & Jim O'Toole
David & Jeannette Besselman	Merrill & Jana Fredricks	Colby Lowers	Curtis W. Perner
Doris D. Boone	Ryan, Brooke, Aubrie & Shelbie Fredricks	Mark & Lindsey Magnus	Velma Poplin
David & Lanetta Burdette	Marybeth & Ike Glass	Jeremy, Shane & Mark Magnus and families	Amanda Ramsey
Dwight & Debra Burdette	Jimmy & Louise Goode	Wade & Tresia Magnus	Regional Dermatology, P.C.
Dwight & Mary Call	Joel & Dorothy Haden	Evelyn Mantooth	Remington Park
Mask S. Callahan	Terri & Paul Hadley	Elizabeth McNown	Rockin' R Ranch
Joyce E. Church	Marila C. Hart	Candy, Chuck & Bri Green	George M. Schull
James M. Coffman	Don Hartley Family	Jockey Eldon Nelson	Harry C. Schull
Joe & Margaret Combs	Kay County Child Care Home Association	Glen E. Nelson, Jr. & Vicki May	Jonathan & Patsy Schull
Drs. Jerimy & Amy Cox	Wade & Shawn Lessert	Glen Nelson, III, Lisa, Chelsea, Lane & Paige	Adele Shackelford
Rick & Cindy Epperson			M. Maxine Sledge
Kyle Epperson			Mike & DeMetra Vap
			The Oscar E. Wells, Jr. Family

In Honor Of

Jennifer Nelson Delaney by Matt & Bonnie Delaney

In Memory Of

My Family—Elisha, Albert & Florence Coffman

Paul & Essie Epperson

Dr. Jim Fuller

Dean & Anna Jacobs by Shirley & Milton Pugh and Jo Beauchamp

Eugene & Maxine Magnus by Randy & Eldonna Magnus, Marcia Magnus & Ragena Dobney and families

Dr. L.L. Merrifield

Eldon & Betty Nelson by Randy & Eldonna Nelson Magnus and family

Eldon Nelson by Lana & Jim O'Toole and family

Ted Wells, Jr. by Randy & Eldonna Nelson Magnus and family

DEDICATION

For Clayton

From day one . . . you believed, without doubt.
Thanks for the happy trails.

The Boys from the Bushes

Lou Dean

FROM THE OKLAHOMA BUSH TRACKS TO THE BIG APPLE

OKLAHOMA HERITAGE ASSOCIATION

CONTENTS

PREFACE

The following book evolved from five years of intense interviews with the last of a vanishing breed. Every fact given, every race, every scene that I recreated came straight from the lives of these bush track riders.

At the end of the editing process, the question of how to categorize this book became an interesting discussion. Because I created dialogue and story lines to make the material more readable, could the book still be classified as nonfiction?

I asked several friends who hold positions of authority in the writing-editing-publishing field about categorizing the book. Each had a different idea.

"It's a historical novel."

"It's a memoir."

"It's creative nonfiction."

After serious consideration, I've decided to let the editors and critics choose any category they like for this work. But, I want you, dear reader, to realize that the following is a collection of true stories about 30 incredible young men and women who charted the course for the racing industry today.

ACKNOWLEDGMENTS

The late Kirk Bjornsgaard, Acquisitions Editor of Regional Studies at the University of Oklahoma Press, is the reason the seed of an idea developed into this book. I nonchalantly mentioned the vague concept for *Boys from the Bushes* to Kirk while speaking at the Red Dirt Book Festival in Shawnee, Oklahoma, in the fall of 2007. At the time, I was in the middle of writing a novel and finishing a memoir. The last thing I expected was an eager editor to follow me down the hallway pursuing the subject. "Lou Dean, I don't think this has been done before. This could be an exciting project."

From the book proposal in late December of 2007 to the first draft of the manuscript in March 2009, Kirk became my encourager. Without his faith in the book, his professional guidance, and his unwavering enthusiasm, I would not have completed the task. Kirk fought his battle with cancer long enough to read the first draft, make a few line edits, and voice his hearty approval.

If Clayton Epperson had not come to hear me speak at the Tonkawa Library in February 2007, the idea for this book would not have surfaced. If he had not later invited me to go to Remington Race Track in Oklahoma City; if we had not ended up in a win picture with Calvin Stone's horse; and if Clayton had not suggested I go with him to Arkansas City to meet his old friend, Charlie Burr. Thank you Cowboy, for your persistent support and enthusiasm. Clayton was gathered in to be with the Lord May 10, 2010.

So many people played serendipitous roles in the completion of this book. On a particularly stressful day while copying win pictures and faded articles of Clayton Epperson and Charlie Burr at a Staples store in Ponca City, a lady standing behind me in line looked down at the racing pictures in my hand and asked, "Who is that?"

Once I embraced the responsibility of shuffling the mountain of resource information for this book, I learned to shut out the little distractions in my life. For instance, I had limited time for idle conversation with curious strangers. I tried to ignore the question, but the lady stepped closer and pointed to a photo. "Do you mind me asking who that is?"

"That's Clayton Epperson," I finally said, turning back to the clerk who handed me change for the copies.

"I know him," the lady replied. "He used to ride with my brother on the bush tracks in the late '40s."

I turned to her and asked, "What was your brother's name?"

"Rabbit Wells."

Her words stunned me. The name Rabbit Wells had come up again and again while interviewing other riders. I had asked many times if anyone knew where Rabbit lived or how I could locate him. I knew only that he, at one time, lived somewhere in Missouri. The pressure of finding missing links to my story had become a gnawing insecurity that had made me want to scrap the project.

What were the odds of Rabbit's sister, Harriett Kendrick, who actually lived 50 miles away appearing in line right behind me at the exact moment I held those photos? I smiled and introduced myself, knowing that I was not alone on my journey.

Thanks to Dr. L.L. Merrifield, who insisted in the fall of 1999 from his deathbed, that I come spend the winters in Oklahoma at his little River House in Osage County and write. Thanks to Jan and the Merrifield family, who allowed me an extended invitation from 2007–2010. Once this project took over, I hunkered down and camped in the house like an unwanted relative. I am indebted to this family for allowing my dogs and me the privilege of a home away from home. Jan, thanks for your unwavering faith in my writing, your friendship, and your unconditional love and support.

My heartfelt gratitude goes to the members of First Christian Church in Ponca City, Oklahoma, and to Pastor Larry Metzger. Week after week, I stepped into your congregation to renew my spirit. Week after week, the special attitude of love and acceptance embraced me and energized me for the next challenge.

Many people at my home in northwest Colorado also made it possible for me to remain so many months in Oklahoma. Thanks to Jeanne Smith for taking such good care of my jackass during many frigid winter months. The four-year endeavor of this book was a lot like us riding across the state of Colorado in 2001 to promote nonviolence in the schools. The journey would not have succeeded without a community of good folks. A special thank you to Red Hinkle and his family for taking care of my house and young trees on Blue Mountain. I lost track of how many times you had to dig out and fix the water line. Only a fellow Okie would stand in the mud and work in 20-below-zero weather to help a friend! Thank you Pat Lollar, another Colorado-Okie, for helping handle the business end of my life in Colorado. Thanks to Heather Zadra at Colorado Northwestern Community College for her initial input during the book proposal stage.

It has been a great honor for me to meet and work with the men and women who are part of this book. Because I relied almost entirely on the memories of the riders, the book would never have been born if Clayton, Charlie, Eldon, and 27 others had not stepped up. All gave their time graciously and unselfishly, patient with my relentless questions, nagging phone calls, and what seemed to be an unending process. Most jumped on board with the same passion that once allowed them to straddle a racehorse, while others I wore down with my relentless pestering. Either way, it was the spirit of each journey that not only kept me writing, but gave wings to the project that otherwise would never have seen flight. Words will never express my sincere gratitude.

Relatives of the deceased riders showed the same spirit of cooperation. Wives, sisters, daughters, sons, and sisters-in-law all were quick to reply to my queries, enthusiastic with stories, and generous with newspaper and magazine clippings. Many, many people, too numerous to mention, gave of their time or offered a brief snippet of information that helped me form the pages of this book. You know who you are. Thank you.

Mildred Burr deserves a special thank you. Not only did she help me interpret what Charlie was trying to communicate while he lay in his bed the last year of his life, but later, while grieving the loss of her beloved husband, she continued to supply me with names, phone numbers, addresses, win pictures, and newspaper clippings. She connected me to Chris McCarron for an endorsement. Any time I asked something of her, she made it her mission to accomplish the task.

Joyce Church, thank you for your rich family history, for sharing your sister's story, for your energy toward the book, for reading the early draft, and giving me a much-needed lift with your eagerness to help promote it in Kansas. Most importantly, thank you for your special faith and for becoming a spirit sister.

Ida Hartley, from day one you invited me into your home, pulled out old win pictures and records, and renewed my sense of humor on the journey. Thank you for taking me under wing, for all of your priceless memories, and for your abiding love for horses and racing.

Wayne and Duane Murty, twin riders now living in Lexington, Kentucky, were the first ones to call my attention to Wantha Davis, one of the earliest women riders of the bush track era. Both also helped me finish Johnny Sellers' biography after his death. Duane, thank you for getting Bobby Ussery on board. Although we have not yet met, from our many phone conversations I've gotten to know and respect the twin bush track riders from Guymon, Oklahoma, who have spent a lifetime in the horse racing industry, and today, in their 70s, are excited about the stable of colts in their barn.

I am grateful to fellow writer and Wrangler Award winner Michael Wallis, who gave generous doses of encouragement and displayed solid faith by telling me, "I will give you a blurb when the time comes." You barely knew me, and yet you took time out of your very busy schedule to make phone calls, send e-mails, and offer suggestions.

Thanks to Ricky Maranon, writer at the *Tulsa World*, who generously passed on contact information for Johnny Sellers' next-of-kin after writing his obituary in July, 2010. Thanks to Sarah Swartz from Ponca City, who brought the article to my attention.

Others who helped me track down essential information or offered brief tidbits include Rich Chamberland; Harvey Phelps; Gene Wilson & Associates of Pond Creek, Oklahoma; Ben Hudson; Frank Holmes; Jack Keathly; Holton Payne; Sam Smith; Linda Davis Clark; Lonnie Colville; and Evelyn Mantooth.

Thank you Eldon Nelson, for starting the "get together" group in Arkansas City during the writing of this book. The special lunches, the memories that spilled out, the camaraderie between Eldon, Clayton, Ida, Joyce, Mildred, and me forever will hold a special place in my heart. The tales that were told, the pictures exchanged, the love, and laughter always energized me to run back to the keyboard and continue working.

I must thank my loyal animal companions, because they have, for many years, remained a strong source of love and nurturing. Thank you Bantam and Keeper for all of the long hours you lay near me as I pecked away behind the laptop. Thanks for reminding me daily to take a break and walk with you. Thanks to, Jinx, the one-time stray cat who stubbornly remained in my Colorado barn on Blue Mountain the four long winters and waited, with faith, for my eventual return. Jesse James, you are the best jackass that ever lived. Thank you for missing me, for welcoming me every summer with a squeak and a sloppy kiss. Thanks for allowing me to slap a saddle on your back upon my return and for your eagerness to climb back up into the serenity of our mountains.

The joy of finally holding this book in my hands will be tinged with sadness because of the passing of Clayton, Charlie, Eldon, Harley, Calvin and Kirk. Charlie, it was a privilege to write your story. I will never forget your struggle, your courage, and your dignity. Eldon, your humble, quiet nature and knowing smile will forever warm my heart. Harley, you called me one week before you passed, asking me if I had found a publisher for the story. You said you had been telling the race trackers at the coffee shop in Sallisaw, Oklahoma, about the upcoming book and were selling many copies. Calvin, thank you for giving me a few words. I really had no idea how difficult it was for you to talk about the past until you opened up "off the record" a few weeks before you left this world. Thanks, Calvin, for your lifetime dedication to horse racing in

Oklahoma. Kirk, your initial passion for the story stayed with me all the way.

Clayton, we both know it was your spirit of contagious enthusiasm that kept me pushing forward, and your unwavering love and support that kept me pressing on. I wish you could hold this book in your hands, but I know that you know.

Thanks to Gini Moore Campbell, Director of Publications and Education for the Oklahoma Heritage Association, for her immediate interest in this project and for printing the excerpt article in their *Oklahoma* Magazine, and for the time and effort to raise the funding for the book.

Frank Holmes, thanks for recognizing the potential of this book and jumping on board. Thanks for connecting me to Dan Streeter, for helping check race records, and your enthusiasm for this effort. Dan, thanks for your many hours of dedication to this project, your patience, and even for the occasional "potshot." It was a pleasure working with you.

Thanks, also, to David Morton for the concept of the front cover. You did an excellent job in helping to capture my vision. I appreciate your patience and commitment.

—Lou Dean
2013

INTRODUCTION

The history of horse racing in Oklahoma is vibrant. From the Comanche Indians wagering horses, deerskins, and weapons on races recorded as early as 1834 and the land rush known as the Last Run of 1893 to pari-mutuel betting at Remington Race Track today, the sport of racing horses in the state of Oklahoma has been passionate and sometimes brutal.

Early in Oklahoma history, unsanctioned races on rural "bush" tracks attracted large crowds. A Jockey Club formed as early as 1870, tracks were scattered throughout Indian Territory, and almost every county fairground had a temporary racetrack. In 1900, horseman associations began to organize in Oklahoma and purses attracted owners from out of state. By 1911, the expanding industry also began to attract gamblers.

The attempt to eliminate or control gambling at the racetracks remained a controversial issue until 1914, when Governor Lee Cruce, with the help of the National Guard, shut down a scheduled race meet at the Tulsa Fairground, thus ending that chapter of rural horse racing history. But nothing could end the passion for horse racing in the state. Oklahoma went on to become not only a hub for racing, but gained a reputation for producing some of the finest Quarter Horses in the world. In 1982 the voters finally legalized pari-mutuel betting.

Forty years before betting was legalized in Oklahoma, when men began returning home from World War II, anti-gambling sentiment temporarily relaxed and the Oklahoma bush track industry exploded. Hundreds of farm boys and a handful of girls with a passion to ride jumped into the untamed arena of the Oklahoma Bush Track Circuit, embracing the dream of becoming a jockey.

These riders were the sons and daughters of farmers, horse owners, and trainers. They rode in moccasins or old shoes and had no helmets, but they were experienced riders with a rugged toughness and a stubborn will to win. Their races were run in pastures, without starting gates, and the finish line often was marked by only a rock or a line scratched in the dirt. Bush tracks often were near barbed-wire fences or dangerous gullies.

This is the story of three boys who were swept up in the tornado of the Oklahoma horse racing frenzy of the 1940s, and thrust into a life of excitement and turmoil before they were old enough to shave. The choices they made and the choices that were made for them led them to become "boys from the bushes."

CHAPTER 1

Earnest Clayton Epperson

Little Epp

Clayton dashed onto the grounds of Jefferson Elementary School just as the last bell shattered the morning silence. Running as fast and quietly as possible down the hall, he tiptoed into the classroom and slid behind his wooden desk. He pulled out his reader and proceeded to follow along as the teacher read, letting his breath slow to a normal rhythm.

He knew the teacher would not scold him. His fourth-grade teacher seemed to accept Clayton's tardiness as part of her daily routine. Maybe she knew him well enough to understand his good intentions.

Clayton tried hard every morning to beat the tardy bell, but no matter how fast he jumped out of bed, slipped into his clothes, and burst out the door, it took time to run the mile from Pine to Thirteenth Street to the horse barn. It took time to feed and water the horses, time to dash back home and eat breakfast, and more time to run the three blocks to school.

His teacher's voice faded into a soft echo as Clayton allowed his mind to wander. In one more day he would be riding his pony, Dinah May, down the main street of Ponca City, Oklahoma, in the famous 101 Ranch Parade. He pictured himself in the crisp new western shirt and jeans his mother had bought for the special occasion. Clayton visualized the floats, the brass bands, and the clowns gathering on the west side of Grand Avenue. He felt his belly pinch with excitement. In his mind, he could see the people on both sides of the street calling his name and waving as he rode by. He might be as famous as Red Ryder, the hero cowboy in his favorite comic book.

As soon as the last bell rang that Friday, Clayton ran home to where he had Dinah May waiting in the back yard. He quickly bridled and saddled the small Paint mare. Jumping up into the saddle and hoisting younger brother Kenny up behind him, he dug his heels into Dinah's flank and reined her back toward Jefferson School.

It was Kenny who had gotten Clayton into this after-school situation by telling the kids about the two of them riding in the parade on Saturday. Naturally, their classmates begged to see the pony and go for a ride.

Clayton trotted Dinah May up to the crowd of kids in the schoolyard, pulled the mare to a stop, and gave his brother a hand off. Clayton kicked his foot out of the stirrup and took the girls first. Pulling them up behind him on the saddle one at a time, he circled Dinah around the school grounds. It made him smile to have a giggling girl latched to his back, begging him to slow down.

But Clayton began to get nervous before everyone had a turn. He cut the last two rides short, explaining that he had extra chores and promising to return another time.

Clayton knew exactly what time his dad, Paul Epperson, got off work at Conoco Oil Company in Ponca City. Because of the parade, his usual Saturday morning job of cleaning stalls and shoveling manure from the corrals would have to be done that afternoon. He would not take any chance of upsetting his father or jeopardizing his ride in the parade.

Sometimes he wondered why his dad always seemed so short-tempered. At 9 years old Clayton wondered about a lot of the "whys" in his young life. Why did his mother return to Oklahoma to give birth to him when the family lived in Michigan? Why did the family later move from Michigan to Ponca City? But Paul Epperson was a driven man trying to provide for his family and had little time for "why" questions in his household. Clayton's dad not only ran a car dealership but worked a full-time job at the Conoco refinery filter house. And although Clayton's mother, Essie, was more understanding, she did not have much time for her oldest boy because new babies seemed to appear every other year. So, by age 9, Clayton had learned to work hard, do what he was told, and keep a low profile.

Paul came into the bedroom the next morning just as the sun blasted through the faded curtains. "Get dressed, boys," he said. "We have to go load Dinah May and start for town soon."

Two hours later, Clayton reined Dinah May down Ponca City's Grand Avenue in the 101 Ranch Parade. Kenny rode behind him. Friends and relatives shouted as Dinah May stepped proudly along. Clayton's crisp shirt itched and his tight boots pinched, but he sat tall in the saddle and grinned.

Later that fall, on a brisk October Sunday, Clayton was helping his dad with the horses at the Ponca City Race Track. By then, Paul, who was a match-race enthusiast,

Clayton, front, with his brother Kenny riding Dinah May in the 101 Ranch Parade in Ponca City, 1945.

had come to realize that Dinah May could run very fast for a short distance. At 50 yards, there were not many horses that could outrun her.

Every Sunday the locals gathered at the rodeo grounds southeast of town for calf roping and various other competitions. After the rodeo, anyone who wanted to match race would throw out a challenge and horse races would be run on the half-mile straightaway bush track next to the rodeo grounds.

On that particular Sunday, Paul had a match race challenge for Dinah May and had begun looking for a jockey when Roger Adair, a local merchant and friend of Paul's, made an offhanded comment.

"Golly, Paul. That oldest boy of yours can ride," he said. "Have you noticed how he sits that little mare?"

Paul's eyes widened. It was not like him to overlook an opportunity. He called Clayton over and told him, "Son, I want you to ride Dinah May in this race."

As Paul borrowed a racing pad from Roger and began cinching it, Clayton's heart hammered double-time.

"Where's my bat?" the boy asked.

He had seen some of the older riders around the track wielding a leather bat to encourage their horses toward the finish line.

"You don't need a bat. Listen . . . ," Paul said.

He lifted Clayton into the saddle, showed him how to position his legs, and then put the reins in his left hand.

"You twist them like this," Paul said. "It's called a half-cross. Then hold onto her mane with your left hand here and your right hand just below until you get out of the gate. Once she leaps out of the gate, turn loose of her mane and you have control."

Clayton was confident. He had ridden Dinah May every day for over a year. He had galloped her down the alley by the barn many times bareback. He could not believe what was happening. He was going to be a jockey.

"Where's my bat?" Clayton asked again.

"You don't need a bat," Paul repeated impatiently. "Here, empty your jeans."

Paul held out his hands and Clayton reached deep into both pockets, placing a few agate marbles, his rusting pocketknife with the broken blade, and his yo-yo into his father's hands.

"Ride her down the track, gallop her back to warm her up, then I'll get you set in the gate," his father instructed.

As Clayton returned and rode Dinah May into the gate, his heart hammered so hard in his ears that he thought his head would explode. He swallowed several times to force the dry knot out of his throat.

Paul Epperson went over the instructions again with a strained tone of impatience as Clayton sat in the gate and tried to listen attentively.

"OK, take the reins, one in each hand, and reach up like this toward the horse's ears," he said. "That leaves a little rainbow in the reins, so after she jumps from the gate you slide your hands back toward you and then you'll have control of her down the track."

Clayton nodded. His heart had settled into a loud thump of determination against his worn cotton shirt.

"When that gate opens, hold on and scream until your tonsils burn," Paul said. "Don't stop screaming until you get past the crowd at the finish line."

Clinging to the reins, Clayton sat trying to remember all of the instructions his dad had given him. He stared out through the V of the two-horse gate. The track looked much different from here than it always had from the sidelines. In front of him was a lane of soft dirt no wider than the 10-foot blade of a road grader. To the left, short posts were driven into the ground about six feet apart, with one board nailed horizontally to make a rail. To the right of the track, across the grass and less than 12 feet away, stood a five-strand barbed-wire fence that ran the entire length of the track.

Clayton pulled his eyes from the ominous possibility of the fence and stared straight ahead, down the track. When the gates banged open, he held on for dear life and yelled. The cheering of the crowd at the finish line grew louder then faded as Dinah May breezed past.

Earnest Clayton Epperson won his first race that day on Dinah May at the Ponca City Bush Track. The excitement of the win lasted long after the roar of approval from the crowd, the slaps on the back and the big grin from his father. That night, while everyone else in the Epperson household slept, young Clayton recreated the race over and over in his mind. It amazed him that the ordinary routine of his life had suddenly taken on such possibility. *He was a rider.*

The following summer, Clayton, now 10 years old, had a full-time job as a jockey. Too small to rein in the powerful horses after the race, Clayton was assigned a cowboy. The volunteer waited near the finish line and bolted his horse up next to "Little Epp's" mount to stop the animal after the race.

"Like Hell I Will"

At age 12, Clayton stood 5' 1" and weighed 85 pounds. With two full summers of experience behind him, he was in demand around the bush tracks. Trainers and owners liked "Little Epp" because he was small, worked hard, and listened closely to what they asked of him.

For $1, Clayton would blow a horse [let it run a short distance as fast as it could run], and for $2 he would break one out of the gate. For a fee of $3 to $5, he would jockey in a match race. Of course, every cent of the money Clayton earned went straight into Paul Epperson's hand. Clayton was the oldest son and was helping out.

Sometimes though, Paul would surprise Clayton with a special reward. Like the day in 1950 when he brought home a jockey saddle from Cowboy Supply in Ponca City. "Son, it's time you had your own gear," Paul said as he handed him the saddle. "This saddle belonged to a professional jockey by the name of Eldon Nelson."

Clayton took the saddle in his lap. It had many years of use but was in good condition. As he held it in his peeling hands, he wondered about the rider who had owned the saddle. Had the jockey met a bad fate with a crippling injury like so many jockeys did every year, or had he retired rich and famous?

For more than a year now, Clayton's hands peeled on a regular basis. He had heard other riders speak of the malady. It had something to do with holding the reins day after day, race after race. Clayton had long since become used to the roughness, but sometimes the appearance of his scaling palms embarrassed him. If he ever met a pretty girl, how could he take her hand into a palm as rough as a piece of crumpled sandpaper?

In fact, he had very little time to think of girls. When he got a break from riding and doing chores, he read Roy Rogers, Gene Autry, and Red Ryder comic books or played basketball with the neighborhood boys.

Turning the saddle in his hands, Clayton examined every inch of it. On the underside of the seat, in black letters, "E. NELSON" was written clearly across the leather. He promised himself he would one day search out the saddle's former owner. Maybe he would even get to shake his hand. Had E. Nelson been an Oklahoma bush rider who went on to become a professional?

Paul was smiling at Essie. He seemed to be in a fine mood, so Clayton asked the question that burned on his lips: "Why would he sell his saddle?"

"Sonny Shultz down at the Cowboy Supply said the jockey, Eldon Nelson, traded it for a stock saddle," Paul said. "I guess Mr. Nelson took a couple of bad spills. I understand his wife had some health problems, so he's decided to quit jockeying. He bought him a ranch north of Cedar Vale, Kansas, and is gonna' raise cows."

Clayton had experienced his share of spills, but he could not imagine anyone ever selling or trading a special saddle because of an injury. He knew that he would never sell this saddle under any circumstances.

In the three years Clayton had ridden for his dad, Paul had bought and sold several horses, quickly becoming a fast study on what made a good racehorse. He seemed to have a keen eye for quality and Clayton could sense that the pursuit of finding "The Racehorse" was in his father's blood.

A little black mare named Stardust was Paul's second endeavor. She already had been raced when she arrived at the Epperson barn. Clayton won on her several times in Newkirk and once at Pond Creek in a six-horse field. Like Dinah May, Stardust had a sweet disposition and was easy to ride.

The day Paul sold the mare to Ben Johnson, Sr., who ran a big ranch near Pawhuska, Oklahoma, Clayton felt a sense of loss. But when he found out that Ben Jr. took Stardust to Hollywood, where she raised several colts, he was excited. In later years, every time he watched a Ben Johnson, Jr. movie, Clayton always looked for the black horse with the star on her forehead that Johnson rode, and would proudly proclaim, "That's one of Stardust's offspring."

Smokey, the third horse Paul brought home, was a ranch horse that supposedly had killed a man.

From the very beginning, Smokey had bouts of temper that erupted unexpectedly. Clayton knew he could not trust the horse and secretly feared him, but Paul had no time for complaints or fear. And although Smokey quickly became his least favorite, in many ways the rank gelding taught Clayton the most.

In a race at Newkirk, Smokey bolted to the outside and threw Clayton over the rail fence into the sandburs. Another time, the rogue pitched Clayton off in a mud hole in the alley behind the barn. Paul always laughed when such things happened.

And so it was Smokey who became the catalyst for Clayton's first rebellion toward his father. On a stormy April morning, Paul told Clayton to blow Smokey out, but keep him off of the track.

"The track's too muddy," he said. "I don't want to mess it up. Blow him out about one-quarter mile down the field."

Clayton looked down at his dad in disbelief.

"You want me to run this maniac out through that uneven field full of chug holes and rocks?"

"Just do it," Paul growled. "Everything will be all right."

"Like hell I will."

The words burst out before Clayton could stop them.

With one quick motion, Paul reached up and slapped Clayton off of the horse. Before the boy could react from that shock, his dad grabbed him by the neck and butt and tossed him right back up on the gelding.

"If I say you will, you will," he threatened.

Rage burned through Clayton like a prairie fire. He took the reins up in his shaking hands and put his feet in the stirrups.

"I hope this horse breaks his neck. I hope I break my neck." The angry words flashed across Clayton's mind, but he did not say them. Instead, he kicked Smokey into a dead run, blowing him out across the rough field, through holes and over rocks, screaming at the horse to give more.

When Clayton returned, with Smokey laboring for breath, Paul flashed a grin.

"I told you everything would be all right," he said. "Take him back to the barn, brace him down, and cool him out."

Clayton's summers blurred into a routine of work and racing. He helped his dad at the Epperson used car dealership, washing cars after school. On Wednesday and

Thursday evenings men would show up at the house and ask if Clayton could go with them to exercise a horse. He would ride down to the nearby Ponca City racetrack and gallop or blow a horse scheduled to run the following Sunday.

Saturdays were spent cleaning the barn and grooming the horses. Sunday afternoons were always on the racetrack. The races alternated between Ponca City, Newkirk, Pawhuska, Fairfax, Pond Creek, and Enid. The first night races were held during that time in Enid.

The bush tracks at Ponca City and Fairfax were half-mile straightaways, mostly for Quarter Horse racing. Pawhuska had a three-quarter-mile round track with an eight-horse gate, where both Quarter Horses and Thoroughbreds ran. Newkirk had an eight-horse gate with a half-mile circular track known in those days as a "bull ring." Although mostly Quarter Horses ran at Newkirk, there often would be two or three Thoroughbred races at the end of the day. Those races would be half-mile and 70 yards and five-eighths of a mile.

Sometimes there would be a special two-day meet at Enid or Pond Creek, which were both half-mile bull rings. Three-day county fair meets were held in Anthony and Burden, Kansas, in late summer. Before Clayton turned 13, Paul began allowing him to drive one of his used cars to the Kansas meets.

At age 12, Clayton did not have a driver's license and was barely tall enough to see over the steering wheel. Paul stacked pillows under Clayton, instructed him to stay at the fairgrounds for the entire three days, sleep in the car, and bring all his winnings home.

The Kansas meets were Clayton's first taste of independence. He loved the feeling of being his own man. The minute he would show up in his 1937 Chevy, word spread fast that Little Epp had arrived. Soon, he would have a full riding schedule each day of the three-day meet.

Clayton, right, at age 13 with his agent, Shorty Burr. Shorty was Charlie Burr's Uncle.

Clayton's only responsibility in Kansas was to ride. In Oklahoma, always under the watchful eye of his father, he seldom had any time for fun. But in Kansas, after the races, he would hang out with friends or find a cute girl and take her to enjoy the fair.

A man named Jess Howard, the only black owner around the race meets at that time, usually brought two Thoroughbred horses to the Burden meet, and Clayton loved to ride them. One of them, Easter Boy, ran in the three-eighths-mile race and the other, Sooner Boy, in the half-mile-and-70-yard race. Howard, who lived in Cleo Springs, Oklahoma, was a respected rodeo cowboy and he treated Clayton well and always complimented him for the rides he put on his horses. He usually brought a pick-up load of ripe watermelons to sell, which added to his popularity.

At the three-day meets in Kansas, most of the riders either slept in the barn or in their car, like Clayton. But some of the older boys would pool their money and share a motel room. Clayton longed to be 16, because then he could go under contract to a trainer and leave Oklahoma. He would ride the professional tracks and become his own boss. Then he would have a pocket full of money, rent his own motel room, and eat cheeseburgers and French fries every day at the cafes.

After the last race each day, it was common to have footraces. Clayton, because of his early habit of running from the barn to school every morning, had grown into a fast sprinter. A man named Forrest Frame from Ponca City became aware of Little Epps' talent and began acting as his agent. He would match Clayton against anyone for 100 yards and then pay Clayton a small percentage of the money.

The fact that this was further exploitation of his talents never occurred to Clayton. He loved to run and compete, and was happy to oblige.

On one such instance in Burden, Kansas, Frame set up a race between Clayton and a champion Kansas high school runner. The odds were against Clayton. When he won, Frame gave him a crisp $100 bill. Clayton took his small fortune, folded it into a two-inch square, and tucked it into the small pocket of his Levis. He had never held back a dime of his winnings from his father, but this, he decided, was different. This money he had won on his own because of his running ability. It had nothing to do with riding horses. He would buy himself a new pair of cowboy boots like some of those he had seen the ranchers and rodeo cowboys wearing. Maybe he would even find a fancy pair like Roy Rogers wore.

In the chaos of his many responsibilities at the track that weekend and the return trip home, Clayton forgot about the money. When Essie washed his jeans the following day, she found the neatly folded $100 bill and confronted Clayton that evening.

"I didn't win it riding," Clayton explained. "I won it in a footrace. I wanted to buy myself a pair of boots."

Essie nodded her head and handed the bill to her young son. Perhaps because she knew Clayton could never have those boots without explaining himself to Paul, Essie said, "Well son, I know you want the boots and you certainly deserve them, but don't you think your dad could put that money to better use for the family?"

Clayton agreed, handing the bill back to his mother, his face flushed with embarrassment. Why had he ever considered such a frivolous idea?

On summer Sundays after dinner, there would always be an important discussion at the Epperson house about who was going to the races that day, and which track they would be traveling to. If they were headed for Newkirk and if Essie was going with the children, Clayton would often ride in the horse trailer with the horses. He would sit up on the feed stall behind the windbreak of the small two-horse trailer, where he could help keep the horses calm. But if they were headed for one of the distant tracks like Pawhuska, Enid, or Pond Creek, and Essie and the younger children were not going, Clayton usually rode in the back of the pickup or even in the cab with Paul.

Attending the races at the Ponca City track meant only a short haul of the horses from their barn, which was less than a quarter-mile from the track.

The horse races in Oklahoma during the bush track era were a social event for people from nearby towns and rural areas. The women would congregate with their youngsters and visit while the men and older boys looked for a match race and then searched for a rider.

There was no way that Clayton, caught up in the excitement of young adulthood, could realize that the era he was growing up in would soon change drastically. In the summer, the iceman made a daily delivery to keep the Epperson icebox cool. The kids watched him carry the ice block with giant tongs, and sometimes he took his pick and chipped small pieces off for Clayton and his siblings. Milk was delivered in glass bottles by milk trucks. Family doctors made house calls to their patients. African Americans went to separate schools and, in Oklahoma, interracial relationships were unheard of.

In May 1945, a month after President Franklin D. Roosevelt died, Harry Truman and the world watched as Japan surrendered. Atomic bombs had been dropped on Hiroshima and Nagasaki, Japan, changing the world forever.

Returning GIs began families, resulting in the post-war Baby Boom. The automobile industry, which had ceased civilian production in 1942, rolled back into full swing. The Big Band sounds of Glenn Miller and Tommy Dorsey blasted from neighborhood radios, and the jitterbug became the latest dance craze. Commercial television became available to the public in 1947.

The scars and losses of World War II, along with the bitter memories of the Great Depression, started to ease and the country embraced much-needed change and new hope. Working mothers and a phenomenon called the "refrigerator" led to frozen meals that in 1947 became known as TV dinners.

As everything in the world changed around him, Little Epp remained focused on his terrain, the Oklahoma bush tracks, and he continued to learn.

Although Clayton loved the intensity of the bigger tracks at Newkirk, Pawhuska, and Enid, he had a fondness for the smaller track in Fairfax, and especially the straightaway track in Ponca City, with its two-horse gate. He had won his first race on that small bush track. He loved to watch the cars line up and park to the east of the track, just outside the barbed-wire fence. He liked the feeling of having his mother, siblings, and friends nearby, watching him ride. He always enjoyed the performances at the rodeo grounds next to the track, where up-and-coming clowns and trick riders practiced their acts.

Because there was no formal means of gambling at the bush tracks, men stood around before the races and wagered. "Betcha' 20 bucks that little bay mare of mine can outrun that gelding of yours for 200 yards." Then bystanders would get in on the bet.

One typical summer Sunday on the Ponca City racetrack, after Clayton helped his dad get the horses to the track and saddled, he mingled with the crowd of men gathering near the two-horse gate. While the roping competition finished in the rodeo arena next to the track, Clayton spoke with owners and trainers, letting them know he was available to ride in certain races. Roger Adair, who in a way had launched Clayton's career, approached the boy to ride his horse, Snickle Breeches. Clayton shook hands to seal the agreement.

Laughter echoed loudly from the nearby rodeo arena, which told Clayton that Sunny, Shorty, and Carl Shultz had arrived to entertain the spectators with their act. He peered off across the track but could not see the donkey in the arena with the bucket sitting on the ground. He did not have to see the routine. He knew it by heart.

Mrs. Shultz, known as Shorty, pumped the donkey's tail as though it was a water pump handle, sending imaginary water into the bucket. Clayton waited as the audience grew quiet. When the second eruption of laughter came, he knew Shorty had taken the bucket and thrown confetti into the crowd. As one of the trainers pulled him aside, he kept one ear tuned for the last burst of laughter, which came when Shorty had thrown her second bucket into the crowd. That bucket had some kind of false bottom, so after Shorty had everyone thinking the bucket contained confetti, she would toss a half-bucket of water into the crowd and drench several unsuspecting kids.

After winning three match races on the Ponca City track that day, Clayton was asked to ride a huge gelding that belonged to Leroy Speakman. The horse, Brownie, was too big to go in the gate, so they "open scored" him. Open scoring was one of many techniques Clayton learned while riding in the bushes. It was the jockeys' job to gallop the two horses toward the starting line, get them as even as possible at the line, and then turn them loose to race. Clayton won the race that day and many other races on the big gelding, who soon mastered the technique of open scoring.

Late that afternoon, a man named Bill Sharp decided to match race his horse, Peppy, against a motorcycle for a hundred yards. Wagers broke the evening silence in a chaotic scramble as Clayton mounted Peppy and listened to Sharp's instructions.

The motorcycle pulled up outside of the gate, even with the starting line. When the starter yelled, "Go," the gateman pulled the gate and they were off.

Even though Peppy was an experienced racehorse, he did not much care for the noisy competition roaring next to him. Clayton talked to him, putting the horse's mind on the business at hand. Peppy pinned his ears and outran the motorcycle.

That evening, the races continued even as the sun set. Someone at the finish line turned on his car's headlights. The finish line judges stood in the light and the races continued into the night.

When someone asked Clayton to open score a horse, race a motorcycle, or ride down a track at night, he agreed with a big grin. Racing at the Ponca City bush track was an adventure. Like the characters in his favorite western comic books, Clayton never really knew what to expect, but he was game for anything.

Charlie Thompson, who then owned the Bar L Ranch south of Ponca City, would sometimes bring Leo Tag to the Ponca Track, stop and get Clayton, and have him blow the horse out of the gates. Sometimes, Bud Warren would drive to Ponca City and take Clayton back to Perry to work his Leo colts, then bring him home.

It never occurred to Clayton that within a decade the bush tracks in Ponca City and Fairfax would be abandoned when racing in north-central Oklahoma shifted to the bigger tracks at Newkirk, Enid, Pond Creek, and Pawhuska. Nor did the young bush track rider have any way of knowing that one day statues would be created in the likeness of and books written about a horse named Leo.

If You Think You Have a Racehorse, Bring it to Newkirk!

A common saying among horsemen statewide during the late '40s and early '50s was, "If you think you have a racehorse, bring it to Newkirk, Oklahoma." The intensity that surrounded the races at Newkirk was nothing like the relaxed atmosphere at the straightaway bush track in Ponca City.

In 1947, the Newkirk Race Track received a major facelift. Formerly used for sulky races, the old facility was rebuilt into a professional bullring track, complete with new barns, an eight-horse starting gate, and bleachers. Akan Pappan took over management of the track sometime after the renovation, becoming secretary, steward, judge, and announcer. Pappan also temporarily filled any other position necessary to keep things running smoothly around the Newkirk track for the next 10 years.

The moment Clayton stepped foot on the Newkirk track, his eyes focused on the barn area. The long shed-row barn filled with stall after stall of horses and the men mingling around those horses always revealed his day's possibilities to ride.

The best trainers at that time were Akan's brother, Alphie Pappan, and Tom Searcy. Clayton knew owners and their horses, like Guy Ray Rutland and Gold King Bailey, sire of the later-famous Pacific Bailey; Russell Burdick and Ponca Blue (Sugar Blue Hancock), Red Connely and Tom Cat; Alley Wilson and Blaze; Bill Sharp and Peppy; Skinner Neff and Fairfax Leo; Fred Swalley and Paleo Pete; and Charlie Thompson and Bar L. Nelleo.

Clayton walked to the barn area and let everyone know he had arrived and was looking for mounts. He mingled around the sign-up table as Akan wrote down the entries, making himself available to anyone looking for a rider.

An hour later, Clayton whistled toward the paddock with his saddle under his arm and the warm Oklahoma wind ruffling his light brown hair. He had a bounce to his step and a big smile on his face that particular Sunday. With Blaze, Ponca Blue, Smokey and Fairfax Leo that day, he would be double-tough to beat.

Because photo-finish capability was still a thing of the future, three judges stood in a box overlooking the finish line to determine the outcome of a race. Sometimes disagreement over the winner erupted and arguments broke out, but for the most part, the judges came to an amicable agreement, and owners and trainers accepted the ruling.

Although it was 40 years before pari-mutuel betting became legal in Oklahoma and there were signs posted right at the track reading NO GAMBLING, during that time the law turned a blind eye to the bookies and the money exchanging hands. The "calcutta" made the gambling seem more innocent. In the calcutta, each horse was "sold" at auction before the race. The highest bidder on the winning horse collected the pot, with 10 percent going to the auctioneer. Sometimes four or five calcuttas were sold for one race, which meant four or five pots.

At most of the races, a bookie let people bet on a horse, and he would set the odds that he would pay. The bookie recorded the name and amount on a card. He paid winners off after the race, usually making a nice profit.

This was also a time when ethics sometimes took a back seat to getting a win. Horses were often drugged on the bush tracks to make them run faster. Back in those days, testing did not take place. Today, a horse leaving the win circle immediately goes to the test barn to have his urine checked for drugs. If any drug is detected, the horse is disqualified. But during the bush track era, no means of testing existed, so drugs were often used, with mixed results. They might give a horse an advantage, but they could just as easily cause it to flip while in the starting gate.

"Machines" also were used to shock a horse into running. A small battery-powered device hidden in the hand would be touched to the horse's neck and an electric shock would send the horse into an adrenaline burst that might propel him forward. Sometimes a horse would buck or run away when a machine hit their neck. Other times, a machine would be effective the first time and never have to be used again.

Horses' names often were changed to give owners an edge. If a horse had won many times and everyone around the track knew the name, the owner would simply change the horse's name to gain odds. That method of cheating worked until someone recognized the horse and spread the word, then the embarrassed owner would have to face the music. Sometimes an owner would change the name and also paint out any white markings on a well-known horse to gain an edge.

Although there were many heated arguments around the racetracks—and a few fist-fights—physical altercations usually did not last long. Bush track racing in Oklahoma, with all of its uncivilized elements, proved to be fairly harmless fun for the hundreds of people who flocked to tracks every summer weekend. In an era before television became affordable to most families, a Sunday at the races was exciting entertainment.

After winning the third race on Smokey that Sunday, Clayton walked the horse to the barn and prepared Paul's special brace of rubbing alcohol, Absorbine Jr., vinegar, and saltpeter. He quickly poured warm water over the horse, scraped off the excess water, then put his father's concoction over Smokey's back, withers, and legs, blanketed the gelding, then walked him.

In the fifth race, Clayton proudly rode Ponca Blue from the paddock where all of the horses were being saddled. As he started down the track toward the starting gate, a blast of wind set up a mini tornado of red dust around him. He closed his eyes and talked to his pony. Ponca Blue did not even flinch. He was no rank beginner.

Riding Ponca Blue into the gate always gave Clayton a thrill, because the horse had his own special style. Unlike many of the half-broke colts Clayton rode, Ponca Blue knew his business. He would walk into the gate with confidence, pick up his front feet, and then plant them just right, and lower his nose into the V of the gate until he had the perfect position. No horse could beat Ponca Blue out of the gate.

By then, Clayton knew the "gate chatter" by heart. Once all of the horses were in the gate, owners would start their nervous talk.

"No Go. No Go."

"Hold It."

"Anytime!"

The second before the gate opened, Paul Epperson would usually whisper to Clayton, "Get Ready."

As his reputation grew, Clayton was given the opportunity to ride some of the champion Oklahoma horses. In one such instance, Clayton rode Fairfax Leo in a famous match race against Ponca Blue at Newkirk and won.

Twelve-year-old Clayton was so excited about the win that day that he went home and wrote a poem. At the time of his death, the framed poem still hung on the wall of Clayton's Ponca City home, along with his class picture at Jefferson school in 1948, when he was 12 years old.

The Match Race of "48"

I'll tell you folks what happened not long ago,
I rode an ole horse by the name of Leo.
He came out of the chute like a bat out of hell,
And first thing I knew, he shot for the rail.

Well, I pulled him back and he chomped along
and then he looked up and thought, "I better get gone."
He passed Ole Blue like a bird in the breeze,
and then he knew, he had got the praise.

Well, I galloped him back "Like a millionaire,"
And all the people standing there, shouted and hollered loud.

Ole Leo was so proud.
He looked up at the crowd as if to say,
"I could do it again just any old day."

I tell you folks, if you want to ride,
Just mount ole Leo, he's my pride.
Skinner and Joe should be two proud men,
to see ole Leo win again. . .
And I hope I'm on him when he runs again.

Fairfax Leo attacked and almost killed Joe Neff in a stall a few years after he outran Ponca Blue in that famous match race at Newkirk. Joe's father, Skinner Neff, called the veterinarian that day and had Fairfax Leo castrated. The horse refused to run from then on. Owners talked for years about the incident and what Fairfax Leo might have accomplished if he had remained a stud.

The race between Fairfax Leo, owned by Neff, and Ponca Blue [out of Sugar Blue Hancock], owned by Tom Searcy and Russell Burdick, was talked about for years around the bush tracks. At that time, Fairfax Leo and Ponca Blue were two of the fastest Quarter Horses on the bush tracks in northern Oklahoma. Unofficial match races during the late '40s were seldom recorded and were often timed using a hand-held timer. Fairfax Leo did set a track record at Pawhuska in 1951, running 250 yards in 13.7.

Clayton later rode Ponca Blue to victory in Enid over Peppy and Blaze.

On June 26, 1949, in a quarter-mile match race at Newkirk Race Track, Clayton raced against jockey Charlie Burr from Arkansas City. Clayton rode Trigger and Charlie rode Snip. The resulting picture, one of the first photo-finishes ever taken by the later-famous Eugene O. "Gene" Wilson of Pond Creek, caused a lot of conversation that day. The race was so close at the finish line that at first glance it was difficult to tell there were two horses. Except for the dual shadows cast on the track, an observer would have thought that the winner had soared over the finish line unchallenged.

Clayton immediately liked Charlie, who teased him about being so slow that day. The two were tough, competitive, and liked to laugh. They became instant best buddies even though Charlie was two years older.

A few months into their friendship, the boys were in another close match race at Newkirk. Clayton rode Tom Cat and Charlie was on Scat Dee. Tom Cat came over and bumped Scat Dee, then won the race. Charlie's Grandma Burr thought Clayton had bumped Charlie on purpose and got fighting mad. She marched onto the track in her long dress and block-heeled shoes, shaking her fist and threatening to whip Clayton.

EUGENE O. "GENE" WILSON
Wilson was born in Pond Creek, Oklahoma, in 1928. In 1946, he was discharged from the Army and returned to Pond Creek, taking up an interest in photography. The Pond Creek racetrack opened in 1947, and Gene started taking win pictures. For many years, he also took photos at weddings, funerals, and family and school gatherings, but by 1961 he turned all of his attention to the racetracks. He did nothing but horseracing win pictures for the next 25 years, taking photo-finish pictures in Oklahoma, Texas, Louisiana, Alabama, Georgia, Tennessee, Illinois, Ohio, Indiana, and Colorado.

Clayton saw Charlie's grandmother storming through the crowd toward the win circle that afternoon and wanted to run. Nothing scared him as much as a woman out of control. Although he was not above winning a race by bumping, that particular afternoon he had not intentionally bumped into Charlie's horse.

Charlie came to Clayton's rescue, assuring his grandmother the bumping had been an accident, bravely saving his new friend from a public flogging. Grandma finally cooled off and later invited Clayton to visit her and Charlie at the family farm near Arkansas City.

The two boys' friendship grew. They competed at Ponca City, Enid, Pond Creek, Pawhuska, and Burden, Kansas, and even though Charlie was nearing 15, 13-year-old Clayton proved to be an equally tough competitor. Clayton went home with Charlie

Charlie Burr and Clayton became friends during a close match race in Newkirk in 1949. Burr on Snip edged out Epperson on Trigger by a nose.

to Grandma's several times and spent the night. For fun, the boys match-raced horses on the dirt road that ran in front of the old farmhouse. Squalling and screaming down the 300-yard straightaway, neck-and-neck, the boys loved to try to outdo each other.

Top: Clayton on Blue Bells following his win at Pawhuska in 1950. Clayton's father, Paul Epperson, held the horse for the photographers. Bottom: Clayton and Blue Bell take first with friend Charlie Burr on Uncle Bob finishing second in Pawhuska.

Sometimes a small crowd of neighbors would watch from the sidelines.

In the evenings, after all of Grandma's chores were done, the two would cruise the main street of Arkansas City and flirt with girls.

In Pawhuska, Oklahoma, on August 6, 1950, Clayton, riding Blue Bells, outran Charlie, on Uncle Bob, by half a length in a three-eighths-mile race. By then, Charlie was under contract back East. Clayton kidded Charlie later that evening, "You better go and tell your agent he has the wrong Okie."

One day in 1951, two years after Clayton and Charlie's first Newkirk match race, Charlie appeared on Clayton's doorstep. Clayton was in the alley playing basketball with a group of neighborhood boys and several members of the Harlem Globetrotters. The neighbors to the north of the Eppersons were a black family named West.

This was three years before integration began in schools across the nation. At that time, blacks in Ponca City resided near "Dixie Hill," which lay south of town, across South Avenue. But Mr. West was the principal of Atex, the all-black school in Dixie Hill. He boldly had managed to cross the line over into what was then considered the "all white" part of town.

As was common in that era, Paul Epperson still referred to blacks as "niggers" when talking about them, but he had learned to like and respect the West family. When friends tried to rub him about his dark-skinned neighbors, Paul refused to debate racial issues.

The Eppersons and Wests slowly became friends. In 1950, Mrs. West made Clayton his first jockey outfit. The day she put the fancy red and white silk shirt and matching silk cap in Clayton's hands, he felt his face blush.

Lately, the men around the track had ranted and raved about the possibility of blacks coming into white schools. Clayton had grown up with the racial lines clearly drawn, but in that moment he did not understand. He loved the

Clayton donning his first silks at the age of 14.

West family as if they were his family. He knew the Wests loved him. Mrs. West had spent days making him a special jockey outfit. For the first time, Clayton would wear his very own "colors." At the bush tracks, none of the owners had silks. The riders wore jeans and worn shirts.

On June 4, 1950, Clayton won a futurity at Newkirk while wearing his colorful silks. The men around the track gave him an award for "Best Dressed Jockey." He could

Top: Clayton with R. Leatherman won "Best Dressed Jockey" in 1950 while sporting his new "silks." Bottom: Jockeys George Washington, Calvin Stone, Bobby Speck, Hershel Radford, and Jackie Myers at Newkirk.

not wait to show the win picture to Mr. and Mrs. West.

The day Charlie came up on the Epperson porch, he must have heard the racket from the alley and peeked around to see his buddy in sweaty competition on the dirt basketball court, lost among a mountain of black men.

"Takin' up a new sport?" Charlie teased, stepping up to Clayton.

"Those are some of the Harlem Globetrotters," Clayton bragged. "They're visiting the Wests."

Charlie nodded, grinning.

"Ask your mom if you can go for a ride with me," he said.

Charlie's smile broadened as he pulled out his wallet and showed off a thick roll of hundred-dollar bills.

The minute Charlie turned 16, he had left the bushes when a trainer named Pete Maxwell offered him a contract to ride at Fairmont Park in Illinois. The day Maxwell took Charlie, he turned to Clayton and said, "I'll be back for you next year."

It was hard for Clayton to believe that just one year after his friend Charlie left the bush tracks of Oklahoma, he had accomplished so much. Neither of the boys knew then that later that year Charlie Burr would be named "Leading Rider of the Nation."

But when Charlie showed up that early spring day, he told Clayton, "Your next, buddy. Pete Maxwell said he is coming after you the day you turn 16. You'll be breaking your maiden in Fairmont Park before you know it."

Charlie had his arm in a cast that April day of 1951.

"They wrapped it in an ace bandage at the track," Charlie told Clayton after retelling the story of the three-horse pile-up that caused his spill. "When Dad picked me up at the airport in Wichita and saw how swollen my arm was, he took me to the doctors in Arkansas City. They cast it."

Charlie grinned and said, "I'll be back at the track in a month. Come on. There's something I want to do and I want you with me."

"Where we goin'?" Clayton asked, following Charlie across the yard.

"Ask me no questions, I'll tell you no lies," was Charlie's reply.

Charlie soon pulled his father's old car onto the Talobott Oldsmobile Car Dealership lot on 2nd Street, between Cleveland and Grand in Ponca City. Both boys were clad in worn Levis and old cowboy boots. Charlie had a cast on his arm. The well-dressed salesman probably thought to himself, "What a pair of country bumpkins."

Charlie took a few steps and stopped dead still when his eyes rested on the shining 1951 Rocket 88 Oldsmobile in the middle of the showroom floor.

It was a slow day, and so the salesman must have decided to have some fun with the two country boys. Maybe he would sharpen his selling techniques.

"Go ahead, open the door and slide in," he said. "She's automatic, top of the line. Get in there and look her over."

Charlie got behind the wheel and Clayton slid into the passenger's seat. They were both grinning from ear to ear, running their rough hands over the soft cloth interior.

"Boys, you're looking at one fine automobile here," the salesman began. "She has a V-8 engine, automatic transmission, radio, heater, and this baby even has factory air-conditioning. She has white sidewall tires and is ready to roll."

"Does it have a spare tire?" Charlie asked, looking up at the salesman as he tinkered with the radio and heater knobs.

"Sure does," the salesman said, motioning for Charlie to follow him. He opened the turtle lid [trunk] to show Charlie the spare.

"What's your askin' price?" Charlie blurted.

"The sticker price is $2,600," the salesman said, "but you look like a couple of honest country boys. Tell you what I'll do. Just for you two, just today, cash on the barrelhead, I'll take $2,150."

With his good hand, Charlie reached into his back pocket for his billfold. He began shelling out hundred-dollar bills onto the hood of the Rocket 88 Oldsmobile.

"I think I'll take her," he said.

Clayton watched the cocky salesman's expression go from smug, to shock, then to complete humility as he mumbled something about paperwork and walked away.

"Come on, buddy," Charlie said. "Let's take her for a spin."

A few minutes later, Charlie drove his two-toned, powder blue and white Rocket 88 off the showroom floor and down Grand Avenue in Ponca City.

"Find us a tune," Charlie said.

Clayton turned the knob on the radio past the soft voice of Nat King Cole singing "Unforgettable," and stopped when the sound of Red Foley came on, singing, "Chattanoogie Shoeshine Boy."

You Aren't in the Bushes Now, Boy

In July, 1951, when Harry Truman was president, Tony Bennett released his first hit, and the average price for gasoline was 37 cents per gallon, 15-year-old Clayton left Oklahoma under contract with Pete Maxwell and headed for Fairmont Park in Illinois. Legally, a jockey had to be 16 to ride on the sanctioned tracks, but Pete was a businessman. He realized Little Epp was an investment that he might lose if he did not take action.

As early as 1950, before Clayton turned 15, owners and trainers started to approach him about a contract. At Pawhuska on August 6, 1950, after winning the three-eighths-mile match race between Blue Bells and Uncle Bob, a doctor approached Clayton about signing a contract. One night at Enid, a Mr. Cook, who owned a construction company in Oklahoma City and had three Man O'War horses—Won A War, War Card and War Falcon—tried to talk Clayton into a commitment.

By June, when Pete Maxwell heard about all of the different owners and trainers chasing Clayton, he decided to make sure that his next bush track prospect did not agree to sign with someone else. Pete made a slight change on Clayton's birth certificate, turning the date of birth from 1936 to 1935 and told Clayton to pack up.

In June 1951, Clayton packed two pair of worn Levis, shorts, t-shirts, and socks into a small suitcase and rode with his family to the Santa Fe train depot in Ponca City. Essie said good-bye to Clayton in the car. Paul walked his oldest son in to buy the train ticket, then stood with him outside of the depot, waiting.

"Son," Paul said, nervously twisting the comic books he was holding for Clayton into a tight roll, "when you get on the train, keep a close eye on your suitcase. And when you get to the track, put it in a safe place. When you get to Fairmont Park. . . ."

Paul seemed to be struggling for words, and he twisted the rolled comic books tighter and tighter.

"A lot of riders will offer you dope," he finally said. "You know what I mean, don't you?"

Clayton nodded, even though he had only a vague concept of what his father was talking about. At that moment he was more concerned about his comic books. Paul had taken Clayton's three new Red Ryder comic books and twisted them into a tight spiral no bigger than a broom handle, and he continued twisting them as he kept talking.

Red Ryder was Clayton's favorite, and the comic books were brand new. Clayton could barely wait to get on the train and read the latest adventures of Red Ryder and his sidekick, Little Beaver. Little Beaver rode a Paint Horse that reminded Clayton a lot of Dinah May.

"You remember your Uncle John?" Paul continued, as he twisted the comic books. "He got started drinking and it ruined his life. You might try that dope and really like it and it will mess up your entire life. Are you listening to me?"

Clayton jerked his glance away from the comic books that were being twisted to shreds, and said, "Yes, sir. I'm listening. I won't try dope."

"That's right," Paul continued. "If one of those older riders gives it to you, tell them 'no.' Tell them you don't need it."

Paul handed the roll of comic books to Clayton and stepped back as the train pulled to a wheezing stop. Clayton was anxious to go. He was leaving home, bound for St. Louis, Missouri, then to Fairmont Park in Collinsville, Illinois. There was a big world outside of Ponca City, and he could not wait to see it.

Pete met Clayton at the train station driving a brand new 1951 Mercury Convertible. However, the excitement of the trip and his arrival at Fairmont dimmed somewhat when Clayton examined his new living quarters.

His room was a small bunk bed in the tack room of Maxwell's barn. Clayton slid his tattered suitcase beneath the bed, put his comic books on an upside-down bucket that would serve as a nightstand and sat on the bed. His furnishings consisted of bridles, saddles, halters, lead shanks, and cooler blankets. A mixture of sweet feed and horse sweat filled his nostrils, and the only sound he heard was the tiny rustle of a mouse somewhere near the foot of his bed.

For a moment, homesickness washed over Clayton. He would not awake to the smell of Essie's biscuits or the sound of his brothers wrestling playfully in the room across from him. All things familiar and secure suddenly had changed. Clayton jumped from the bed and walked out into the barn. There, Pete had 16 or 17 horses. Clayton's first challenge was to learn what he could about his new mounts.

Clayton's day began at 5:00 every morning. He had until 10:00 a.m. to gallop, breeze, and work those horses in the gates. At 10, the tractors and harrows began preparing the track for the races to be run later that evening. After that five hours of work, Clayton helped with chores at the barn and took horses to the creek or to graze on nearby grass using a lead shank. By late afternoon, he began getting his instructions from Pete on the races for that night.

On the few occasions he had a break from his many duties, Clayton would walk to a little café outside the gate, eat a cheeseburger, and play the pinball machine.

Clayton had been to Fairmont Park less than a week before he broke his maiden. In that week, he had learned to pay close attention to Maxwell's instructions before each race. By then, Clayton realized he still had a lot to learn about riding Thoroughbred horses.

The first reprimand he received from Pete was for riding a horse "from gate to wire." Unlike Quarter Horses, Thoroughbreds do not run at a dead run from the gate to the finish line. Clayton began learning the fine art of "rating a horse," or keeping the horse in hand and releasing him at the crucial moment.

The morning of his maiden race, Pete rode the track with Clayton.

"Clayton, tonight you'll be riding a 5-year-old mare named Hunter's Pride," Pete said. "Stay about four feet off of the rail because you can see how deep it is."

That evening, he talked to Clayton again in the paddock.

"Hustle her away from the gate and get a good position going into that first turn," he said. "Stay about four feet off of the rail, like I said. If someone starts coming up on the inside, let her go on. Keep her in hand. When you get on the backside by the half-mile pole, shake your stick, and bring her home."

Pete looked back at Clayton as he tightened the cinch on the saddle. Clayton nodded his head.

But Clayton knew by then that instructions only go so far, then come circumstances. He had done exactly what Pete told him to do, but coming up on the half-mile

Clayton won on Hunter's Pride at Illinois' Fairground Park. Left to right, standing, Lance Cross, Ranch Owner from Cheyenne, Oklahoma, trainer Pete Maxwell, and an unidentified horse shoer.

pole he found himself in a pocket. The jockey on his right turned and sneered, "Going somewhere, rider?" There were horses in front of him and to the outside. He had no place to go, so he used an old bush track technique and slowly allowed Hunter's Pride to drift out, crowding the rider to his immediate right.

The jockey on his right yelled, "Take ahold of her."

"That's what I'm trying to do," Clayton answered, but by then he had successfully scooted the horse far enough to shoot through the hole. He lifted her head and let her roll, winning by a head.

In the race that day, a horse from Chicago named Play Arm was a 25-to-1 long-shot. The gangsters intended Play Arm to win so they could collect those odds. The little rider from Oklahoma had upset their plan. Clayton heard rumblings of threats that he did not really understand.

He also was called in and chastised by the stewards, one of whom said, "You came across a little too quick, Epp. You aren't in the bushes now, boy. Watch yourself." Clayton understood the warning, but his trainer had told him to get a good position, so he had let his horse run wide open, cutting in front of some horses to get that position to the first turn. Of course, he knew that many of the tricks he had used in Oklahoma were not allowed on the sanctioned tracks, but the adjustments to the bigger world of racing did not scare him. He had won his first race on a sanctioned track, broke his maiden.

The emotional high of the win was replaced with sudden dread when he entered the jockeys' room. Like every other male fraternity, jockeys had certain traditions. When a young rider broke his maiden, the professionals would take him down and paint his privates with shoe polish!

That evening, after the excitement and chaos of the day ended, Clayton settled into his cot with the familiar sound of horses in the stalls nearby munching hay. This was when the aching homesickness for his family always hit him. During the day he was much too busy to think about anything but work. He wondered how Essie was do-ing with Baby Billy. He could picture his younger brothers out in the back yard playing cowboys and Indians and see his little sisters stretched out on the living room floor with paper dolls.

When he called home the week before, Essie told him that younger brother Kenny had begun to ride in Clayton's absence. Clayton hoped his dad would not be too rough on Kenny.

Clayton allowed himself only a few brief moments to luxuriate in the longing for home, however. If he spent too much time looking back, he had difficulty going to sleep. Instead, he replayed his day. Then he turned his thoughts to Charlie Burr.

On August 16, 1951 in Burden, Kansas, Clayton won the 440-yard-race on Good Eye outrunning younger brother Kenny on Maizy Doatze.

Charlie had broken his maiden on that exact same track, riding a horse for Pete named Thomas. Later, Charlie also won on Hunter's Pride. But today, Clayton had ridden Hunter's Pride that same mile-and-a-sixteenth in a second-faster time than Charlie had run. He grinned. Wait until he saw Charlie again.

"Look out buddy," Clayton said out loud into the darkness. "I'm right behind you."

Less than a month after Clayton arrived at Fairmont Park, he found himself boarding the train to return to Ponca City. While grazing two horses on lead shanks out near the creek, one horse cow-kicked and caught Clayton below the left kneecap, leaving a hole about a half-inch deep. He would not be riding for awhile.

Disappointed, he wanted to stay and do what he could until he could ride again, but Pete assured Clayton he could return to Fairmont Park.

"Go home and stay off of that leg," Pete said. "If you don't, it may be a year before you ride again. If you take care of it, I'll be sending for you soon."

One afternoon before Clayton left Fairmont Park, a stranger approached him at the barn. "Gene Ellis, who owns Ellis Park, is interested in you, young man," the stranger said. "Mr. Ellis would give you a car and a cabin on the lake if you will come back and ride for him. Just think about it."

The man gave Clayton a phone number and then disappeared.

Clayton won the 3-furlong race on Little Joe beating Kenny on Easter Boy. Clayton said the mare's name was not really Little Joe as it was a common practice during this era to change the name of a fast horse. Left to right, standing, Kenny Epperson, unidentified, Shorty Burr holding the horse, and possible owner A. Lewis.

Clayton did not pay much attention to the offer. He was committed to Pete and at that time was reeling with disappointment about having to leave Fairmont Park. But once he reached Ponca City,

Clayton's spirit quickly rebounded. It was good to be home. He would recover. He would return to Fairmont Park.

Younger brother Kenny had stepped into Clayton's shoes and was riding Paul's horses. Kenny asked Clayton to at least ride along to the meets and offer support, so within a few weeks Clayton stood up on the bad knee and began saddling horses in the paddock, walking them into the starting gate, and leading them to and from the barns.

By August, Clayton was back in the saddle. Although his knee was still stiff, he decided to put it to the test at the meet in Burden, Kansas. Because Kenny was running in three races, Clayton took mounts in the same three races, teasing Kenny that he would not have a chance.

On August 16, 1951, Clayton won the 440-yard race on a horse named Good Eye, outrunning Kenny who rode Maizy Doatze. Clayton won the three-furlong race on Little Joe, outrunning Kenny on Easter Boy. And big brother Clayton, on Sooner Boy in the four-and-one-half-long furlong race, outran younger brother Kenny on Johnny Red.

In all three pictures, Kenny stood in the win pictures with a strained mixture of pride and disappointment on his face. It would have been nice to win a race, but here was his big brother who had broken his maiden at Fairmont Park.

The biggest thrill for Clayton that day was the win on Good Eye. He had won on the horse many times. He felt a special fondness for the animal that really did have

Clayton in Burden, Kansas, won riding Sooner Boy with brother Kenny took second on Johnnie Red.

Left to right, standing, owner Jess Howard, unidentified, Kenny Epperson, and Shorty Burr

Owner Les Kunkel holding horse, Kenny Epperson to his right, and Shorty Burr behind Kenny. Other unidentified.

On October 13, 1951 at Chisholm Trail Park in Pond Creek, Oklahoma, Clayton won on Bonnie Scotland.

only one good eye. As long as they gave Good Eye the rail, he proved to the world that his disability meant nothing. Later, Clayton rode and won on Good Eye at Newkirk, in a quarter-mile race, when the gelding was 17 years old. The owner, Mr. Kelley, announced before the race that day that Good Eye was going into retirement.

After the meet in Burden, Clayton was convinced he was fit to ride again. He could barely wait to get home and call Pete Maxwell. But to Clayton's disappointment, Pete told him it was too late to return to Fairmont Park that year, adding "You just take care of that knee and we'll talk next spring."

KENNETH PAUL "KENNY" EPPERSON

Epperson rode the bush tracks until 1953. Riding at Newkirk, Pond Creek, Pawhuska, Fairfax, and Enid in Oklahoma, Kenny also competed at Anthony and Burden, Kansas. He rode with Rabbit Wells, Johnny Garroutte, Terry Truman, and Willie Hunt, as well as most of the other riders at that time. He climbed up on some of the best horses, including Dyna Flow Miss, Kanzo, Fairfax Leo, Kay County Bill, Ponca Blue, Peppy, Leolita, Silver Thistle, King B, Vandy Reed, Lady Scott, and Scotchman's Pride. He won the third running of the Kansas Futurity in Meade, Kansas, on Vandy Reed in 1953 and later trained horses for his father before becoming an owner and trainer. He was well liked around the Oklahoma bush tracks.

Kenny Epperson wins on Dyna Flow Miss in 1953 in Enid, Oklahoma. Ray Fagan is holding horse. Above, brother, Clayton on the rail on Kansu.

The Trainer of Trainers

Kenneth finally got the best of Clayton in a 330-yard purse race run on May 8, 1952, in Enid, Oklahoma. Kenneth rode Dyna Flow Miss to a win over brother Clayton, who rode Kanzo. Dyna Flow Miss later became the dam of AQHA champion 2-year-old filly Dyna Go Miss.

Within a month after that Enid race, Clayton left Ponca City for the East Coast. He had hooked up with a fellow rider, Rolli Poulter, and was going to travel with him to Wheeling, West Virginia. Local owners Walter and Guy Shultz had a string of horses in Wheeling and had asked Clayton to come ride for them.

As he was leaving home once again, Clayton kissed Essie, who had 1-year-old Billy on her hip, hugged his little sisters Joyce and Sue, and shook hands with his father and brothers Kenny, Leroy, and Ronald. Before he stepped into Poulter's station wagon, Clayton turned back and winked at Kenny.

"You can be in the win circle for awhile, little brother," he said.

Walter and Guy Shultz had several horses stabled in the barns in Wheeling. Clayton slept in the sleeping quarters in the Shultz's trailer the night he arrived, and the next morning began galloping horses. One special horse, Butch K, later became famous, and a race would be named in his honor at Ak-Sar-Ben Race Track in Nebraska.

One day, Clayton went to the track office in Wheeling with Walter Shultz to go under contract to ride his horses at a meet. After doing some checking, the staff there told him that he was still under contract to Pete Maxwell. Clayton would have to get a release from Pete before he could ride for Walter. Because Clayton had not heard anything from Pete in the spring of 1952, he assumed the contract had ended.

Clayton was told that Pete Maxwell was training horses in Hamilton, Ohio, and that before he could ride anywhere, Clayton would have to get a release.

The next day, Clayton ran into a friend and fellow bush track rider, Rabbit Wells from Ponca City. Rabbit invited Clayton up to an apartment that he and several riders shared. While Clayton told Rabbit about his problem, Bill Dockerty, an agent, overheard the story.

"Clayton," Bill said, "I'll take you to Ohio and get you a release from your contract."

The following morning Clayton packed his gear and suitcase into Bill's yellow 1952 Buick convertible and the two headed down the highway bound for Ohio. When Clayton walked into the training barns and Pete saw him, a big smile came across his face. "Am I glad to see you," he said.

But the smile faded when Clayton told him he had come to ask for a release so he could ride in West Virginia. After a pause, Pete said, "Clayton, I usually make Leading Trainer here. I'd like for you to stay and ride for me."

The opportunity to win a lot of races appealed to Clayton, but now Bill was pressuring him to get the release. He decided to think it over and stayed for three days, galloping and working horses for Pete.

On the fourth day, Bill came to Clayton and told him that Pete had given them the release.

"I told him you had an itch to go to Atlantic City and compete with your Buddy, Charlie Burr," Bill said.

As Clayton was packing to leave, a man came to the barn and cornered him.

"I hear you rode in the bushes and you know how to open score," he said.

Clayton grinned. "Yeah, I know how to open score a horse."

So Clayton rode with the man over to Dade Park, Kentucky, and won the open-score three-quarter-mile race. The man gave Clayton $50 for that day.

As Clayton and Bill left Hamilton, Bill said, "Let's go on up to Atlantic City and visit your buddy Charlie Burr. We'll see what kind of opportunity there is up-state."

The idea of seeing Charlie excited Clayton. Maybe there was a place for him in Atlantic City. Maybe before the summer was over, he would be competing against Charlie, like old times.

Charlie Burr was riding for Hirsch Jacobs when Clayton showed up. He immediately got Clayton a job working and galloping horses for Hirsch.

Excited to see his buddy, Charlie proceeded to make plans for both of them for the year. "We can go from here down to Hialeah, Gulf Stream or Tropical Park in Florida, and ride this winter," he said. "Just think, the two of us competing again."

"Now the world will see who is really the best," Clayton teased.

One day, Clayton ran into Joyce Riggs on the backside of the racetrack. She was a girl jockey he had ridden against back in Anthony, Kansas. Her father was running horses at Atlantic City. No matter how much Clayton's world grew and changed, familiar faces from the bush tracks continued to turn up everywhere.

Caught up in the fun and excitement of being his own boss, Clayton jumped into every opportunity that came along. He galloped and worked some horses for Colonel Marcus, who had the track-record-setting Duke Omar and his full sister, Duchess Omar.

Colonel Marcus liked Clayton and asked him to go under contract. Right before Clayton signed that contract, however, Bill pulled him out of the office.

"Have you signed anything yet?" he asked.

"No, I was getting ready to sign," Clayton replied.

"Don't sign anything." Bill's voice was shrill with excitement. "I just talked to Sunny Jim] Fitzsimmons. I told him all about you and he said to have your little hind-end up at Aqueduct Park in New York at 5:00 a.m. tomorrow morning."

Clayton agreed not to sign. Although he had heard of the great Sunny Jim, he really did not understand the opportunity that had mysteriously fallen into his lap. Why would Sunny Jim Fitzsimmons be interested in a bug boy from the bush tracks?

If he had learned anything, though, Clayton knew that being a jockey was a crazy profession, made up of lucky breaks and the right horses. There were no guarantees, and contracts were signed and broken every day. The year before he was on top of the world one minute, breaking his maiden at Fairmont Park. A week later he had boarded a train to return to Ponca City, Oklahoma.

Late that afternoon, Clayton found Charlie sitting in the kitchen near the jock's room, having a sandwich and coffee.

"I have something to tell you," Clayton said. "But I don't want to tell you in here." The room was noisy with jockeys and trainers, loud conversations, and the bantering over a pool game in the corner of the room.

"What are those guys doing?" Clayton asked, pointing to three men setting up a large camera on a tripod in the corner of the jock's room.

"Some news reporters from Philadelphia. I guess they've come to film jockeys during their leisure time," Charlie chuckled. "Speaking of leisure, have you made it down to the Boardwalk yet?"

"No," Clayton said. "Let's take off as soon as we're done today."

That evening, the excitement of the Atlantic City Boardwalk caused Clayton to temporarily forget his big news. He walked along, caught up in the magic of the mass of humanity. Lyrics from a new Hank Thompson song ran through his mind: "the glamour of the gay night lights has lured you." He understood for the first time exactly what the words meant. The bright lights of the Boardwalk were intoxicating. They held a certain electric excitement that he had never before experienced.

On one side of the Boardwalk, the waves of the Atlantic Ocean slapped in a hypnotic rhythm that caused Clayton to stare out across the endless water. He breathed the salty air deep into his lungs, and the moonlit water beckoned to him with a siren call. He had seen pictures of great whales, sea turtles, and giant squid, but until now had not been able to imagine such creatures actually existed in the depths of the ocean.

On the other side of the Boardwalk, an endless array of businesses clamored to the passersby with every form of advertising imaginable. Towering above it all, lighted billboards displayed the names of entertainers like Louie Armstrong, Dean Martin, and Jerry Lewis. Above the sound of the boys' boots tapping against the Boardwalk came loud music, screams of laughter, and the call of vendors selling peanuts, popcorn and hot dogs.

Charlie and Clayton stopped near a huge crowd of people waiting to see a lady jump a spotted pony off of a high platform into a small pool of water near the beach. Amazingly, the horse jumped, splashed, and the show ended with screams of disbelief and thundering applause as horse and rider emerged from the pool unharmed.

"You reckon you'd have the nerve to jump your pony off of that platform?" Charlie asked.

"Maybe," Clayton said, looking up and considering the possibility. "Maybe not."

Charlie laughed. "So what's the big news? Did you work out a deal with Hirsch Jacobs? Are we gonna' ride together all summer and go to Florida this winter?"

It was time for Clayton to make the announcement. The two stopped walking and leaned against the railing. Clayton lit a cigarette and inhaled deeply, then blew the smoke into the salty air. Seagulls were squalling all around them, diving and fighting over popcorn and food morsels dropped on the beach by the steady stream of people below.

"Bill talked to Sunny Jim Fitzsimmons this morning," Clayton said. "I'm leaving in about an hour to head north. I'm supposed to be at Aqueduct Race Track at 5:00 in the morning."

Clayton was anxious to hear Charlie's response. By then, Charlie knew who was who around the Big Apple. He would know if Aqueduct was a wise decision.

Charlie stared at Clayton as if he could not comprehend the words. His demeanor changed from fun-loving to dead serious.

"Clayton, Mr. Fitzsimmons is the trainer of trainers," he said. "There are jockeys that would give anything to just gallop a horse for him. Hell, I'd give an arm myself, if I could go on riding with one arm."

Charlie grinned and stuck out his hand.

"I guess it's goodbye for now, buddy," he said. "Good Luck."

A Colt Named Nashua

Later that evening, Bill Dockerty and Clayton started down the Pennsylvania Turnpike on their way to New York City. Clayton turned the dial on the radio until he heard the familiar voice of Hank Williams, singing his latest hit, "Your Cheatin' Heart."

After riding for miles to the music, Clayton turned the radio down.

"Did you hear that Eddie Arcaro just won his fifth Kentucky Derby?" he asked Bill. "He rode a horse called Hill Gail."

Bill nodded, but did not seem much in the mood to talk horses, so Clayton turned the radio back up and settled into the seat to the sound of Patti Page singing "Mockin' Bird Hill." As the lights of New York City appeared in the distance, Clayton promised himself that one day he would win six Kentucky Derbys and break Eddie Arcaro's record.

Early the next morning, Bill and Clayton pulled up to the guard gate at the backside of Aqueduct Race Track, where the stables were. Bill told the guard why they were there.

The guard said he had been notified about them arriving, and that "he" would be pulling up to the barn anytime. Bill and Clayton waited. Within minutes, a big black limousine pulled up in front of the office across from them, near several long barns. The guard told Bill to drive in and go on down toward the car. The back door of the limo opened and a stooped old man got out, cane in his hand.

"That's him," Bill whispered to Clayton. "That's the famous Sunny Jim Fitzsimmons who was recently in *Who's Who* magazine."

Clayton's first impression of Sunny Jim was of sympathy. The ancient man, dressed in what looked like wool army pants with rubber bands around the cuffs of the britches, looked like a common beggar. If he had not just stepped out of a limousine, Clayton would have reached into his Levi's and handed the old man a quarter for a cup of coffee.

Sunny Jim greeted Bill and Clayton with a "good morning" and started walking toward the barn. Bill and Clayton followed. The old man picked up a clipboard at the end of one of the barns and walked on. Horses soon started appearing out of the long shed-row barn's doorway. As eight or 10 horses walked by, Sunny Jim would tell each rider what he wanted them to do on the track.

He motioned for Bill to stand with him by the track's outside rail while he watched each horse work.

Clayton knew from experience that trainers did not like to be bothered when they concentrated on the morning workout, so he hung back and sat on a bench, watching each horse work. Sunny Jim would look over at him every once in awhile. Clayton got the uncomfortable feeling that Bill was telling Sunny Jim about him. Sitting under the close scrutiny made him nervous. Clayton was not used to sitting or waiting.

All of a sudden, Sunny Jim turned and motioned to Clayton.

"Son, I understand you've ridden more than a thousand races in the bushes," he said.

"Yes, sir," Clayton replied. "I reckon that's true."

"See that barn?" Sunny Jim asked, pointing. "Walk inside and there will be a horse saddled, waiting for you."

"Yes, sir!" Clayton said eagerly.

As he approached the barn, Clayton saw a sign reading "BELAIR STABLE." A man stood in the shed row with a horse saddled and bridled. Clayton walked up to him and said, "I'm Clayton Epperson. Is he mine?"

"Climb aboard," the man replied.

He got Clayton's left leg and lifted him up. As Clayton set his stirrups and tied his reins, he felt someone watching. He looked quickly over his shoulder and saw the bent shadow of Sunny Jim in the doorway. The old trainer was watching Clayton's every move. The handler led the horse to the doorway and turned Clayton loose with his mount.

Two riders on horses circled around Sunny Jim as Clayton emerged from the barn. He watched as Sunny Jim told each rider what he wanted them to do on the track, then he rode over to get his instructions.

"Gallop him once around the track," Sunny Jim said.

"Yes, sir," Clayton replied.

As he started onto the track, Charlie's words from the night before floated back to him: "Mr. Fitzsimmons is the trainer of trainers. There are jockeys that would give anything just to gallop a horse for him."

The memory made Clayton smile. He breathed in a deep lungful of the crisp morning air and put his mind on the business at hand.

After Clayton galloped the first horse around the track and brought him back around to where Sunny Jim stood, a man took the horse by the bridle.

"There's another one waiting for you in the barn," Sunny Jim remarked.

Clayton rode three horses that day. The first one he took in a two-minute clip gallop. The second horse he worked a half-mile, letting him run. The third he worked five-eighths of a mile to the wire, in hand.

JAMES EDWARD "SUNNY JIM" FITZSIMMONS

Fitzsimmons was a Thoroughbred racehorse trainer with American Classic Wins at the Kentucky Derby—1930, 1935, and 1939; Preakness Stakes—1930, 1932, 1935, 1936, 1939, and 1955; Belmont Stakes—1930, 1932, 1935, 1936, 1939, and 1955. His was inducted into the United States Racing Hall of Fame and the National Turf Writer's Association's named the Mr. Fitz Award in his honor. His significant horses included Hard Tack, Seabiscuit, Gallant Fox, Granville, Omaha, Johnstown, Nashua, Misty Morn, and Bold Ruler.

Fitzsimmons began his career in 1885, working as a stable boy. He spent 10 years trying to succeed as a jockey, but constantly had to fight his weight. His career as a trainer spanned 70 years and he produced 2,275 winners. The great "Sunny Jim" trained two U.S. Triple Crown Champions—Gallant Fox in 1930 and Omaha in 1935. He also trained Bold Ruler, who sired Secretariat.

James Edward "Sunny Jim" Fitzsimmons about the time Clayton rode for him.

When Clayton brought the third horse back, Sunny Jim asked him if he could be there at 5:00 a.m. the next day.

"Yes, sir," Clayton replied.

He rode back to the barn, sitting straight and proud in the saddle.

When Clayton arrived at the barn on the second morning, Sunny Jim told him there was a horse waiting for him.

"Hilarious is the best stallion in the barn, but we have to put him in front of the set because he's a little ornery," Sunny Jim said.

Clayton immediately got nervous. He was not afraid of any horse, but he never had ridden horses of this quality. This would be a true test of his skill and courage. He focused his attention on Sunny Jim's instructions.

"Gallop him once around the track," the trainer said. "Stop him at the five-eighths pole, trot him up to the half-mile pole, and work him in hand to the wire."

As Clayton rode the big stallion to the backside of the track, his hands trembled slightly on the reins. Hilarious was a stakes horse. This ride could be the turning point in his entire career. If Sunny Jim was impressed with his skill, Clayton might actually have an opportunity to ride for the *trainer of trainers*.

Clayton forced his fearful thoughts to the side. He remembered all of those wins on the bush tracks.

"Charlie, Buddy, here I come," he said to himself as he dropped Hilarious down at the half-mile pole and realized tears were rolling down his cheeks. He never had been on an animal with that kind of speed. When he rose to pull the stallion up, Clayton said a quick prayer. "Lord, don't let him take a bad step." He pulled him up slowly and soon they were walking back toward the barn.

Sunny Jim stood watching. Clayton was sure he saw a slight smile play at the corners of the old man's mouth.

Later, Clayton learned that Sunny Jim had gallop boys work a horse the day the horse was going to race. And he heard from one of the grooms that Hilarious had just won the $100,000 Tremont Stakes at Aqueduct Park. Could it be possible that he would soon ride such a horse into the winner's circle?

The thrill of riding that kind of champion filled Clayton's days with magic. Sometimes, on brisk early mornings, riding one of the powerful Thoroughbreds onto the track seemed like a lingering dream. He had gone to sleep in the small house in Ponca City and awakened to a fantasy. Like Dorothy in the *Wizard of Oz*, he was on an adventure in another world.

But dream or reality, Clayton realized he had been given a rare opportunity to learn. Each day when he finished his riding responsibilities, he concentrated on his surroundings. He soaked up everything, from the activity of the grooms and gallop boys to the names and records of the horses in the barn.

Sunny Jim took each horse's temperature every morning. If a horse had even one degree of fever, he did not go to the track that day. The trainer also kept a daily chart on each horse in his barn. Each morning, Sunny Jim spent time studying his records. It was clear to Clayton that part of the secret to Sunny Jim's success was the simple fact that he worked very hard and always knew everything about each individual horse in his barn.

Every week, bunches of carrots arrived at the barns and would be hung on the walls outside each stall. The grooms would cut the fresh carrots into small bites and mix them with the horses' feed. On Friday evenings, every horse got a special hot-bran mash.

Two stalls at the end of the barn were "mud stalls." Sunny Jim instructed the grooms to keep the stalls wet down until each contained six or more inches of fresh mud. Every few days, each horse would be put in the mud stall for the day to help condition his hooves and keep them from cracking.

One afternoon, about a week after Clayton arrived, Sunny Jim asked him to come into his office. Sunny Jim excused himself to answer the telephone, leaving now-16-year-old Clayton to look in awe at the pictures on the office walls. Seeing the photos of Sunny Jim with presidents, movie stars, and Triple Crown horses made Clayton edgy. When he was with the old man on the track, he related to him as a trainer and a nice man, but seeing Sunny Jim in the company of royalty temporarily unnerved the Oklahoma bush track rider.

In the corner of the spacious office, Clayton noticed a replica of a horse's lower leg standing on a bronze plate. He stared, wondering, when he heard Sunny Jim's voice behind him.

"That is an exact replica of the hoof and lower leg of Dark Secret, who broke his leg one-quarter of a mile from the finish line in the Jockey Club Gold Cup in 1934. When the jockey felt the leg give, he stood up on Dark Secret to rein him in, but the horse refused to quit. On a broken leg, he outran a good horse named Faireno. Dark Secret had to be destroyed after the race."

Sunny Jim stood in silence for a moment, then said "I keep that to remind me it's the heart that makes a true champion."

Clayton looked from Sunny Jim to the bronze leg. He had been told many times that the measure of a champion had nothing to do with the size of the horse and everything to do with the size of the heart. Having heard it now from the trainer of trainers, he would never forget.

"What would you say if we let Bill Dockerty go on about his business?" Sunny Jim asked. "I don't think we need him now. I believe I can find a place for you here." Sunny Jim said the words in a matter-of-fact way that caught Clayton off guard.

"But, Bill's the one that brought me here, sir," he said.

"Would you like to stay?" Sunny Jim asked.

"Yes, sir."

Sunny Jim smiled, as if he were pleased with Clayton's response.

The next day, when Bill came to say goodbye, he seemed happy to be leaving. Clayton wondered later what kind of agreement Bill had made with Sunny Jim. Knowing agents he had dealt with in the past, he suspected Bill had been compensated.

That night in bed before he dozed off, he wondered how, of all the great riders around, he had made it to Long Island, New York, to ride for the famous Sunny Jim. Did it have something to do with Charlie Burr getting Leading Rider of the Nation the year before, and Clayton's close relationship to Charlie? Had some mystical word gotten somehow to Sunny Jim about a fresh bug boy with great talent? It was a question that would forever remain a mystery.

Sunny Jim arranged for Clayton to stay at an apartment house owned by the Shipleys on Long Island, not far from the racetrack. Clayton settled right into his routine with the help of the Shipley family and another rider who lived upstairs. The other jockey drove Clayton to and from the track each day.

Most mornings, the two would stop at a café close to the track and have breakfast.

One morning at the café, Clayton saw an attractive blonde sitting with a black man. In Oklahoma in the 1950s, there was no such thing as an interracial couple. Clayton's alarm showed on his blushing cheeks. He got up and started toward the booth where the blonde sat with the black man.

The jockey grabbed him from behind. "What are you doing?" he asked.

"Maybe she's in trouble!" Clayton said.

"No, man. You see mixed couples all of the time up here. Get used to it."

Clayton sat down and ordered breakfast, trying to wrap his mind around the jockey's words.

"A few years ago, a black man was hanged in Tonkawa, Oklahoma, for being seen with a white girl," Clayton explained.

The rider looked at him in disbelief, then said, "This is a different world up here, Clayton. People don't get hanged for doing what they want to do."

Clayton thought about the rider's reply as he ate his bacon and eggs. He also thought about Mr. and Mrs. West, the black couple who had lived next to his family on Sixth Street. He remembered the day Mrs. West handed him the jockey outfit she had made for him. He thought about the love he always had felt from her and for her. Those feelings always contradicted a lot of what he had learned while growing up.

He realized that the instant animosity he felt toward the black man sitting in the booth with the blonde came from things he had heard others say, things he never really had understood.

"So, do you still wear guns on your hips down in Oklahoma, and chase wild Indians, too?" The rider was grinning.

"Sure," Clayton said, glad for the opportunity to change the subject. "I leave my guns in my suitcase."

The jockey looked at the serious expression on Clayton's face. "Are you pretty fast?" he asked.

"You want to see?" Clayton asked.

When the young man's eyes widened, Clayton could not hold back his laugh.

Although most of Clayton's time was spent riding that summer, he occasionally helped the grooms cool out horses. One of the grooms took a shine to him and invited Clayton and several other riders to go crabbing late one afternoon.

Clayton stood at the foot of the Statue of Liberty and watched the groom throw in his four-sided trap. Within minutes, the groom pulled out a trap full of the crawling creatures that somehow reminded Clayton of Oklahoma tarantulas. The groom took the riders to his house and boiled the crabs.

Clayton refused the offering, saying "Thanks, but I'm more of a hamburger and French fry man."

The riders looked at the groom, and then all of them tackled Clayton on the couch and stuffed some crab in his mouth. Clayton was surprised that it tasted so good and agreed to have more.

One day after riding, Clayton stopped to visit with Sunny Jim's brother at the barn. Tom Fitzsimmons ran the heat machine on the horses' legs. Clayton stood and watched silently until Tom looked up and smiled.

"Hold your hand down here, Epp," he said. "Hold it about an inch away from the inside of his leg."

Tom held some kind of electric pad along the outside of the horse's leg, between the knee and ankle. "Can you feel anything?"

Clayton was amazed to feel heat come right through the horse's leg and warm his fingers.

"I can feel the heat on my hand, Tom," Clayton said. "That penetrates good."

"Takes care of a lot of sore muscles," Tom explained.

After a few minutes, Tom stood and stretched his back.

"Young man, you have it made," he said. "The old man thinks a lot of you."

Clayton's face reddened. He was not prepared for such a nice compliment, and not equipped to know the proper reaction. After an awkward silence he stuttered, "Thank you, sir." Then he turned immediately and walked away.

Tom's words warmed Clayton the rest of that day. He had never received much in the way of respect from his father, so it was difficult to trust such praise at first. But when Tom told him that Sunny Jim liked him and that he had it made, Clayton remembered something that he had overheard the week before.

Sunny Jim was gently scolding one of the younger riders as Clayton walked up from behind, saying "Take him in hand, but then talk to him, like Epp does. 'Easy boy . . . Easy.'"

When Clayton heard Sunny Jim using him as a good example, he was confused at first. It was difficult to believe that someone like the great Sunny Jim Fitzsimmons could respect a bug boy from the Oklahoma bushes. But after what Tom said, Clayton slowly began to believe that Sunny Jim actually cared about him, and the reality of that caring made Clayton's confidence soar.

On a special day, Sunny Jim took Clayton with him to the horse farm in up-state New York, where the young horses were broke and gate trained. As they walked through the stables, Sunny Jim pointed out certain horses.

"You see that filly right there?" he said. "I think she's going to be a good one. She's a full sister to Hilarious."

Farther down the breezeway, Clayton peeked in at a colt that frolicked and kicked around the stall, causing his mama to pin her ears. Clayton laughed, "You'll be away from your mama soon enough, big boy."

"We call him Nashua," Sunny Jim said, pausing to watch the playful colt. "Something tells me that name will go down in history. Who knows, son, maybe you will be the one riding him."

The thrill of that possibility made Clayton stand in silence for several minutes and admire the colt.

One morning after Clayton worked horses, Sunny Jim pulled him aside. "Clayton, I want you to meet someone who's training at a barn close by," he said. "I've got three barns full of horses, but this guy has only two horses, Black Type and Combat Boots. I'm thinking what we will do is put you under contract with him temporarily. Then you will be free to ride my horses when I can get you on. You see, my owners will ask for established jockeys, like Arcaro. We'll have to ease you into this."

As Clayton and Sunny Jim walked into the trainer's barn, Clayton noticed a bantam rooster sitting on the door of Combat Boots' stall. He stopped and stared.

"That rooster is his stable mate," Sunny Jim explained. "He stays in the stall with him, and when the horse travels, the rooster is close by."

Sunny Jim introduced Clayton to the trainer, and then they talked for a while. On the walk back Clayton said, "Mr. Fitzsimmons, I guess you are the greatest trainer that's ever lived."

Sunny Jim stopped and smiled, "Son, I'm 78 years old and I'm still learning."

Late that summer, Paul Epperson called from Ponca City and told Clayton he needed to return home for school.

"Dad, I'm riding for Sunny Jim Fitzsimmons," Clayton said. "He wants me to stay here."

"No," said Paul. "You get on home, you hear? Don't make me have to come get you."

Clayton felt the weight of the world come down on his slender shoulders. He tried to think of a way around his father's demand, but later that morning, still reeling with disappointment, he went to Sunny Jim.

"Let's call him," Sunny Jim offered. "I'll talk to him."

Clayton fidgeted his dusty cowboy boots against the floor as he listened to Sunny Jim's conversation with his father. First his heart would leap with hope and then fall in despair.

"Mr. Epperson, I'll see that this boy goes to school right here," Sunny Jim said. "I'll make sure he graduates."

There was a long pause and Clayton leaned closer into the doorway, waiting.

"But, Mr. Epperson, this boy can make enough money in one year to fill a boxcar if you'll let him stay." There was a long pause. "I see. Well, I wish you would reconsider."

Sunny Jim hung up the phone slowly. Clayton stood in the doorway and dipped his head. He knew his father would always have the last word, no matter what. Clayton was a minor. Even though his birth certificate proclaimed his age to be 17, he had just turned 16 in April. It would be two years before he could make his own decisions. He knew his father would come after him if he refused to return.

Sunny Jim got slowly up from his desk.

"Son, you go on back to Oklahoma and finish school, then come back," he said. "We'll pick right up where we left off. And if you go back down there and fill up on mashed potatoes and gravy and get too big to ride, come back anyway. I'll make you an assistant trainer and give you a string of horses."

The kind words of encouragement did little to soften the blow. At that moment, nothing could cool the anger that smoldered deep in the pit of Clayton's gut. Paul had thrown him up on a horse when he was 8 years old, pushed and prodded him to be the best. Clayton had worked hard, very hard to please his father. Now, after eight years of effort, with the opportunity of a lifetime in his lap and for reasons Clayton would never fully understand, Paul had simply and quickly pulled the rug out from under him.

Sunny Jim followed Clayton back toward the barn, "Have you been reducing any?" he asked.

"No," Clayton said, still in a state of shock that he would soon be returning to Ponca City. Still fuming with hot anger.

"Well, Clayton, I don't want you reducing," Sunny Jim said. "I was a jockey once. I had to reduce. I'd run around the racetrack in a rubber suit, then go into the tack room and cover up with an Army blanket and sweat. One day after I put myself through that routine, I got a deep chill and my muscles contracted and drew up. I believe that was the beginning of this crippling arthritis I have today. I don't want you reducing."

Clayton listened half-heartedly, feeling as though he might be sick. He would have to pack that night and the next day get on a bus for Oklahoma. He had awakened from the beautiful dream.

"Did you hear me, son. I don't want you reducing," Sunny Jim repeated.

"Yes, sir," Clayton agreed.

It was years later before Clayton realized the full meaning of Sunny Jim's words that day. The trainer truly *did* care about him. He not only respected him both as a rider and a person, but he had true concern about Clayton's health and his future.

In the fall of 1952, when Clayton returned to Oklahoma, he clung to the dream that, once he graduated, he would return to New York. But Clayton was held back in school the year his folks moved from Michigan to Oklahoma. And because of time missed for riding every spring, he had struggled academically and been held back again.

In the spring of 1953, Clayton found out he would only be a sophomore the following school season. At 17, he had grown two inches, gained weight, and was getting too big to ride. Both graduation and the dream to return to New York began to unravel.

Two years after Clayton returned to Oklahoma, in 1954, he heard the news from back East that a bay colt named Nashua entered eight races, winning six and finishing second twice, a performance that earned him champion 2-year-old honors. Clayton remembered clearly the day Sunny Jim had taken him to the barn and he had asked about the bay colt. If he had stayed in New York, he could very well have been the jockey riding Nashua to fame. The bitterness over Paul making him leave New York smoldered to a burning ember, and Clayton did not speak to his father for days.

Essie cornered Clayton one day out by the barn.

"I can only imagine how angry you are right now, son," she said. "Please try to understand that in his own way, your dad wanted what was best for you. He's always

By 1954, Clayton had started training horses when he became too heavy to ride. Owner V. L. Payne, holding horse, at Newkirk, with Clayton to his right. Oscar "Rabbit" Wells on Kay County Bill. Other unidentified.

On May 8, 1952 at a night race in Enid, Oklahoma, Clayton won a 3-furlong race with a time of 36.2 on Joe Peter for a purse of $100.

been . . ." Essie's eyes filled and she lowered her head. "Too damned hard on you."

Clayton never had heard his mother say a curse word. He stopped unloading bales of hay from the trailer and stared at her.

"That's because you are your father's son," she continued. "He sees himself in you. Maybe someday, when you become a parent, you'll understand."

Father & Sons

Clayton first saw Phyllis Thompson outside the Ponca City High School, talking to a girlfriend. He took one look at the blonde country girl in her long poodle skirt and bobby socks, heard her soft, drawling voice, and fell instantly in love. Clayton went home that afternoon and told Essie, "I just saw the girl I'm going to marry."

In 1956, the last year Elvis could walk down the street without being recognized, Clayton married Phyllis. They graduated together from Ponca City High School and Clayton's future quickly shifted from dreams of the racetrack to life as a family man. He worked a retail milk route for Meadow Gold Dairy for two years. He became a welder and for years repaired oil and grain tanks. He worked in Wichita, Kansas, for Boeing Aircraft as a certified welder. He became a control man for the Continental Carbon plant in Ponca City, where he worked for 30 years.

Clayton and Phyllis had two children, Diana Lynn and Clayton Alan. Clayton lost his beloved wife of 50 years on October 3, 2006.

While working a full-time job and raising a family, Clayton also trained and raced Quarter Horses in Oklahoma and surrounding states. And Clayton continued to help his father pursue his dream of finding *the* racehorse.

From Newkirk, Oklahoma, to La Mesa Park, New Mexico, Clayton led horses into the winner's circle for the better part of three decades. The men he worked with at Continental Carbon affectionately called him "Racehorse."

Paul Epperson, in the meantime, had purchased a filly from John Ladner in Ponca City, named Bobby Bud. Fred Whittaker from Fairfax, owner of the great Joak, saw Bobby Bud at Newkirk as a 2-year-old and immediately fell in love with her.

"How much will you take for that filly, Paul?" Fred asked.

"She's not for sale," Paul would say.

Then one day, Hunky Tallchief, who was a regular around the Pawhuska racetrack, said, "Anyone that wants a horse that bad . . . you should let him buy her, Paul." Hunky apparently had heard Fred asking Paul several times about Bobby Bud.

So, Paul went over to Fairfax, to Fred Whittaker's ranch. Fred took Paul around and showed him all of his new Joak babies.

"I'll give you $600 and any baby except the one over there," Fred offered.

"I don't want that one," Paul said immediately. "I want that little sorrel with the bald face."

The filly's name was Lady Scott.

One day in the late fall of 1960, Paul pulled into the Newkirk racetrack, parked, and watched his three oldest boys, Clayton, Kenny, and Leroy, unload his sorrel mare. As a 2-year-old, Lady Scott already had proven her speed to be AAA, but Paul still delighted in bringing his pride and joy to the Newkirk track to outrun the competition.

Ida Hartley always knew when the Eppersons arrived, because invariably someone around her table would look up and curse, "There's those blankety-blank Eppersons with that damned mare."

That Sunday afternoon, as Lady Scott backed out of the trailer, Clayton noticed a large crowd of men gathered near the south side of the horse barn. He wondered if some kid had been kicked.

One of the locals walked toward him, grinning.

"What's going on over at the barn?" Clayton asked.

"They've brought in a horse today to outrun your mare," said the man.

"Who?" Clayton asked, curious.

"They've brought Dynago Miss from Purcell, Oklahoma. Mr. A.B. Green is standing over there right now."

"Couldn't be Dynago Miss," Clayton said, then thought "Dynago Miss was the 1960 Champion Quarter Running 2-year–old Filly."

"I don't know, but she's standing over there in a stall," the man said.

Top: Bobby Bud, ridden by Bud Carter at Pawhuska. This is the mare Paul Epperson later traded Fred Whittaker for Lady Scott. Bottom: Paul Epperson holding mare and Kenny far right, others unidentified.

Clayton followed his dad and two brothers toward the barn, weaving through the crowd gathered around the end stall. Standing outside the stall, in an immaculately pressed suit, expensive boots, and western hat was A.B. Green.

"Mr. Epperson," A.B. said, "I've come up here today to run you a horse race. I want to run it for $10,000."

Clayton's dad looked shocked.

Paul replied, "I don't have $10,000. But I've entered my mare in that open race. Maybe there would be somebody here who would like to bet that you can't win."

Immediately, a local man spoke up, saying, "I got a hundred dollars says you can't outrun Lady Scott."

"I have $200," another replied.

A roar of bets boiled out as the crowd moved in and clamored to get in on some of

Top: Harley Crosby in 1960 winning on Lady Scott at Newkirk. The next generation of bush track riders got their start on horses owned and trained by the Eppersons. Bottom: Kenny holding Lady Scott.

the action.

"Wait . . . I'll take your bets," Mr. Green said. "Where do I enter?"

Paul smiled slowly and said, "Ida Hartley, sitting right over there at that table."

Ida Hartley's raspy voice called out across the yard, "You better hurry. I'm closing the books. If you don't get your name in before I draw, you've lost out."

Ida began to shake her pillbox that contained the eight wooden numbered "pills" about the size of dice. Each owner stepped forward.

"Last call," Ida shouted.

While this was going on, Clayton walked to the end stall, Kenny and Leroy beside him. There, a sorrel filly with a new leather halter stood calmly looking back at him. A brass nameplate on the halter proclaimed "DYNAGO MISS."

Paul led Lady Scott to the paddock that day, and held the reins while Clayton saddled the mare. The clamoring from the stands quieted to a hush as Clayton led Lady Scott out of the paddock with a rider whose last name was Courtwright in the irons. He frequently rode for the Eppersons.

"I'll meet you at the starting gates," Paul said after giving Courtwright his instructions.

The hush of the crowd became a buzz as the horses warmed up on the track. Fingers pointed and the names "Lady Scott" and "Dynago Miss" echoed clearly out over the wind. The intensity of the excitement took Clayton back to his glory days in the saddle. He wished he could be the one in the irons for this special race.

The men around the starting gate still were talking about who would win and exchanging money. Calvin Stone's voice rose above the chatter, "I'll bet anyone $100 that Lady Scott will be first out of the gate."

Clayton smiled and wondered how much Calvin already had bet on Lady Scott.

Lady Scott wore the number 5 on the right side of her bridle. The numbers helped in case a photo finish was needed to determine the winner. In this instance, Clayton thought the race might be too close to call and the photo would determine the outcome.

Paul rode in the bed of the pickup along the outside of the racetrack and up to the starting gates. As Courtwright rode Lady Scott toward the gate, Paul grabbed her by the bit and walked her in a circle, waiting to load. Orie Meeks started loading the horses.

"Number one," he called out. "Number three and five. Number two is loaded. Number four is going in."

Clayton shuffled his feet nervously near the outside rail at the finish line. Once the gate banged, the race would end in less than 30 seconds. He exchanged an intense

IDA & DON HARTLEY

The Hartleys ran the Newkirk Race Track from 1959 to 1962. After three years at Newkirk with no problems from the local authorities, the Kay County Sheriff arrived one Sunday in 1962 and said there would be no more races. "There's an old Blue Law against gambling, and I have to enforce it. The racetrack is officially closed."

The Hartleys took their horses and went on the circuit to Ohio, Kentucky, Michigan, and Illinois. They returned to Oklahoma and ran the Pawhuska Race Track from 1975 until 1980.

Ida and Don Hartley, second and third from left, Calvin Stone, on ground behind horse, and Hartley children Jim and Gloria, right, at Newkirk in 1963.

look with Kenny and Leroy. This could very well be the greatest race ever run at the Newkirk track.

When Paul had Lady Scott relaxed in the gate, he moved her forward, positioning her nose toward the front, and then told Courtwright, "Get ready for the break."

Paul noticed a man standing outside the rail about 10 yards down from the gate and wondered if Calvin Stone had asked someone to judge who broke out of the gate first, so there would be no arguments.

The noise in the crowd lowered, and for a few seconds Clayton heard nothing but the gusting Oklahoma wind. A small cyclone of red dust trailed gently down the track behind the starting gates, and just as it traveled up to the horses' rumps, Orie pulled the rope and the gates banged open.

Lady Scott broke from the number five hole on top by a half-neck and roared down the track, straight as an arrow. The crowd of more than 500 erupted briefly, then calmed. A thin cloud of dust hung in the air from the gates to the finish line. For a moment, no one knew for sure who won, then the crowd erupted into a screaming frenzy. Their favorite, the hometown horse, had outrun the out-of-town challenger by at least a length.

Top: Paul Epperson's Lady Scott won the Ben Johnson Memorial on May 14, 1961 in a time of 17.7 for 300 yards. Painted Joe Jr. took second. Bottom: By 1961, Clayton was training for his dad and others while working a full-time job. J. Robinson on Lady Scott, Clayton holding banner on left, and brother Leroy on right, with Epperson family and friends.

From the gate, Paul ran toward the finish line. He knew Lady Scott broke first. He could see her two lengths in front down the stretch, but then the dust had obscured his vision. In the distance, he saw his three sons run out onto the track, and then he knew.

Courtwright galloped Lady Scott up as the Epperson men, women, and children gathered in the winner's circle.

"What a filly!" Courtwright exclaimed to Paul. *"What A Filly!"*

It always had been one of the Epperson boys who walked the horse down the

Top: March 3, 1961 at La Messa Park, New Mexico, Lady Scott ran 400 yards in 21:3 beating Bell's Pudding. Bottom: Clayton holding horse, brother Leroy, right, and Pete Herrera on Lady Scott.

MASTER CHARLES
CLAYTON EPPERSON OWNER   REAL KIPTY 2ND
JACK BALDWIN TRAINER   ITS MOON BAILEY 3RD
JOHNNY HOUSTON UP   400 YDS   SEPT 19, 1985   TIME :20.63

Top: In 1985, Clayton's horse, Master Charles, trained by Jack Baldwin, won a 400-yard race in 20:63. Bottom: Clayton, wearing straw hat and glasses, and his wife, Phyllis with her purse over her shoulder.

track after a race, but that day Paul proudly led Lady Scott back to the barn. With each step he thought, "My mare just outran the Champion Filly of the Year, a filly out of Go Man Go."

     A.B. Green, swarmed by a gang of locals who were eager to collect their bets,

SIDS BOU SAID

2   CLAYTON EPPERSON OWNER   OKIE CHALLENGE 2ND
     JACK BALDWIN TRAINER   JO BE ONE 3RD
     JOHNNY HOUSTON UP   350 YDS   MAY 15, 1987   TIME :18.09

Clayton's horse, Sids Bou Said, wins at Blue Ribbon Downs in 1987.

approached Paul near the barn. Turning, A.B. pulled out his checkbook and waved it in the air to assure the men asking for their money. But before he began writing checks, he turned back to Paul.

"Mr. Epperson," he said, "I'll give you $25,000 for that blaze-faced sorrel mare right now."

Paul grinned and shook his head.

"I'll give you $50,000," A.B. offered.

"Mr. Green, she's not for sale for $100,000," Paul said, then he turned to Clayton and gave him Lady Scott's reins. Paul hesitated. Clayton knew an extraordinary moment in the history of his father's life had just taken place. As he took the reins, Clayton noticed, for the first time, that his father's thinning hair had turned completely white.

"Son, would you take our filly and cool her out?" Paul asked.

	Haymow Bob - 2nd	**HERE COMES MARV**	Boyd Caster - Trainer
REMINGTON PARK	Wild Taste - 3rd	B.g.5 Here We Come - Scurry by Gato Del Sol - Bred in OK by Beth Caster	Martin Escobar - Jockey
RACING • CASINO	7 Furlongs in 1:23.44	Wanda B. Stone - Owner	Purse $31,200 August 18, 2007

August 18, 2007 at Remington Park in Oklahoma City. Clayton Epperson invited the author, Lou Dean, to attend races. When a horse owned by fellow bush track rider Calvin Stone won the race, Lou Dean and Clayton got in the win picture. That led to a discussion of the bush track era, and the idea for this book was born. Behind the horse, second from right Clayton in white tennis shoes, Lou Dean to his right, and Jim Walker. far right. Others unidentified.

Scotchman's Pride

BEAUTIFUL RED DUN FOAL OF 1964

Joak

Sire of many Rom running horses and great broodmare sire as well.

Scott Lady

Dam of 3 AAA. All by Joak;
  Scotchman's Pride,
  Lady Scott,
  Scott's Day,

This horse ran AAAT at Los Alomitos, Laredo, Texas, and Raton, N.M. He o u t r a n some of the best horses in training, such as Barbara 3; Rainbow Derby Winner, Mr. Rocket Bar, One of the best on the West Coast, Dial Three Bar winner of Evangeline Downs Futurity outrunning All American Winner, Go Dick Go, and many more top horses to numerous to mention.

Scotchman's Pride's full sister, Lady Scott, is further proof of the p r o t e n c y of this cross; having outran some of the best horses of her time, such as Dynago Miss; world champion two year old filly, Idle Hour; world champion three year old colt, Kaystorm, Iron Maiden, Tonto Ginger Avavia Dial, Sports Page, Phaebe Ack, and many more.

Scotty's Day, another full brother of Scotchman's Pride, was a good solid AAA campaigner. He is well known for taking the measure of the great AAAT mare Hi B Hind an Oklahoma Derby winner in a special match race ran at Newkirk, Oklahoma.

Where else can you breed to a horse of this caliber at a low introductory fee of $250.00 with a $50.00 booking fee.

Veternarian available at all times. Live foal or return guaranteed $1.00 a day mare care.

Standing at the Johnson ranch 6 miles East & ½ mile South on the Pioneer Woman road Rural Rt. 2 Ponca City, Oklahoma

Paul Epperson, Owner
Office Phone A.C. 405 RO5-3916
Ranch Phone A.C. 405 RO5-7920

The pride of the Epperson family, Scotchman's Pride.

CHAPTER 2

Charles Edwin Burr

Grandma's Farm

Charlie Burr herded the milk cows into the corral with a slap of his hands. Every day started and ended in the dark. With more than 20 head of cows to milk morning and night, a dozen pigs to slop, and chickens to feed, work was an endless cycle in 11-year-old Charlie's life.

With his butt on the milking stool, his head in a cow's flank, and both hands squeezing a teat, Charlie allowed his thoughts to come and go at will. The news Grandma had given him the day before filled him with awe.

"Son, you will one day own half of the cows and everything on the farm, including the farm itself," Grandma had said over supper, just as Charlie was loading his plate with green beans, new potatoes, and cornbread.

He looked up into his Grandma's eyes.

Left to right, in Arkansas City near the farm, Shorty Burr (Charlie's uncle), Charlie, and Grandma Burr.

"You've been here two years now, and worked hard," said Theresa Burr, who everyone called Grandma whether related by blood or not. "If it weren't for you, I would have lost everything. In my book, that makes us partners."

As the words echoed back across Charlie's memory, he talked to the restless cow that had lifted one back hoof a few inches off the ground and threatened to kick.

"Settle down now," he said with authority, lowering his tone to sound like his dad. At 11 years of age, Charlie suddenly felt like a man. He was now part owner of a farm, 26 cows, and three horses.

The cow placed her hoof back on the barn floor and relaxed, munching her grain. Charlie's hands pumped the teats, sending strong streams of milk into the metal pail. His thoughts jumped farther into the past at the sound of the milk hitting the bucket.

Two years before, at age 9, he had been a little boy. Charlie's transition into manhood began the evening his father, Art Burr, told him he would have to leave home on South Fifth Street in Arkansas City, Kansas, and move down the road to Grandma's farm. The year was 1943, and with World War II raging, sacrifices were being made everywhere.

"Son, your Uncle Shorty has joined the Navy and gone off to fight in the war," he had said. "My mother is alone now on the farm, with cows to milk. With me being the oldest son of the family, it's my responsibility to help her. Since I have my hands full here, . . ."

Charlie had listened carefully to his father's words and wondered what was coming. He remembered the hesitation before his dad made the announcement.

Stopping his fork in mid-air, Charlie stared across the table at his mother's eyes. The familiar expression of hard anger that both confused and saddened him was ever present. Esther's bouts of violent temper had long since become a source of agony for Charlie. Sometimes it seemed to him that his mother lived to berate him. Regardless of who started what, he was the one who usually got whipped. But maybe Esther's eruptions had nothing to do with him at all.

Charlie had once overheard his father and uncle speak of the family tragedy that occurred when Charlie was only a year old. His 2-year-old brother, Arthur, and his first cousin, Betty Lee, had drowned in the Walnut River. The two golden-haired cousins had apparently toddled out of the yard one evening when Charlie's mother and father were visiting with his aunt and uncle. The women were preparing a meal and the men chopping wood when the youngsters suddenly disappeared.

Whether the children had been tossing stones into the water and slipped down the bank or had tried to wade and been overcome by the shock of the icy stream was never known. Thoughts of the sad mystery hung in Charlie's mind long after he overheard the conversation. Even at the tender age of 9, the reality of what his parents must have gone through helped young Charlie accept and even embrace his mother's rage.

That evening at the supper table, when his father cleared his throat to continue, Charlie quickly looked from his mother's squinted stare to his father's softer eyes, and waited for his dad to finish the announcement. His father was stern, but even-tempered and quiet. If it was the loss of Charlie's brother that had permanently darkened his mother's mood, Charlie was thankful it had not affected his father the same way.

"Son, since you are the oldest boy in the family, it's your responsibility to go live with your grandmother and help her run the farm until Uncle Shorty returns," Art explained. "On Saturday, we'll gather up your things and get you settled in."

The news left Charlie spinning with questions he knew better than to ask. His father had told him how it would be. Any argument or questions would probably send his mother into a fit of rage. Charlie waited a few moments for the words to settle over him. His younger brother, Gene, sitting next to him, gently touched his foot to Charlie's under the table. Charlie forked a huge bite of biscuit and gravy into his mouth and gave Gene a nudge of response with his shoulder. Charlie often exchanged the silent communication of kicks and nudges with his three brothers and one sister in response to their parents' conversations over supper.

Settling in at Grandma's had been a brief shuffle of his clothes and few words spoken.

"You'll be fine, son," Art assured him, giving Charlie's narrow shoulder one quick squeeze of assurance. "I'll be down the street."

Charlie made the transition without fussing, but those first few days at Grandma's he was amazed at how homesick he became. He missed his old bed and talking to his brothers and his sister late at night when the cold Kansas wind banged against the loose windows. He even missed his mother's temper. But he especially missed those bright moments when his dad would lift Esther out of her dark mood and she would lighten the Burr house with laughter.

Life at Grandma's was an endless list of chores, which gave Charlie little time to brood. In the beginning, he was afraid of the bossy old cows that threatened him with lowered heads and raised hind legs. He felt awkward on the milk stool and could not make his fingers pull the milk from the cold teats, but Grandma was patient with him.

He soon learned the tricks of corralling the cows. He learned which ones kicked, which ones would try to be difficult and the ones that cooperated from start to finish. Charlie knew how to take a difficult cow in between good-natured cows in order to speed the milking process so he could get to nearby Washington Elementary School on time.

Grandma worked side by side with Charlie. She helped bring the cows up, with the milking, and clean the barn. She cooked him big meals, took care of his clothes, and never failed to praise the hard work he did.

Those first few weeks, Charlie's hands ached from milking, his lower back stung from the strain of sitting on the wooden stool, and he suffered several kicks from mean cows that left him bruised and battered. In the beginning, getting up at 4 in the morning made Charlie so sleepy at school that he often dozed off and then was sent to the corner, a punishment he hated worse than a lashing.

Sometimes, sitting with his head buried in a cow's flank, Charlie had cried softly for the carefree days of being at home. His daily chores at home had been nothing compared to his work now. But within two months, Charlie accepted his routine without complaint. His body hardened, his mind toughened, and he embraced his new life with a mature attitude. After all, he was a man, doing a man's job.

His grandmother's affection and loyalty eased Charlie's transition from childhood into manhood. She needed him. She appreciated everything he did. Unlike his mother, Grandma was patient, loving, and kind.

In fact, Grandma was kind to most everyone. If someone needed help, young or old, she would lend a hand. At times, Charlie felt as if he had moved into a boarding house. He would go to bed at night with just Grandma in the farmhouse. The next morning, several other people would be sleeping here and there. Grandma would feed them breakfast before they went on their way. Some days there would be eight or 10 people to stumble over and share supper with, but it gave Charlie a warm feeling to be part of his grandmother's compassion.

Of course, Grandma had her personality quirks. She seldom hid the fact that she preferred the company of boys and men.

"Women draw flies," she would say, jokingly.

Grandma, in her long skirts and block-heeled shoes, also had a tough side that stepped boldly forward anytime there was an altercation. Theresa Burr and her daughter-in-law, Esther, had their share of heated arguments. Charlie's mother and grandmother were like oil and water. Both women were strong-minded and temperamental. Both liked being in charge.

On one occasion after Charlie moved in with Grandma, he got kicked out of school. In his attempt to stay ahead of the farm work and his schoolwork, Charlie often struggled academically. One day, in exasperation, a teacher slapped Charlie in the face with a book. Charlie, who by then had learned to fight and take care of himself, hit the teacher back and was expelled.

Grandma did not tell Esther about the incident, but when Charlie's mother heard about her son being kicked out of school, she stomped over to Grandma's farm, boiling mad.

"What is going on that Charlie isn't in school? You need to get him back in school right now," Esther screamed from the front porch.

Charlie, who was pouring milk into cans, heard his mother. He leaned close to the barn door and listened.

"That stupid teacher hit him right in the face with a book," Grandma shouted, standing in the house holding the screen door open. "I'm glad Charlie hit him. I wanted to go up there and hit him myself. Charlie doesn't have to go back to that damned school if he doesn't want to."

Charlie grinned from his hiding place in the barn. Other angry words were shouted before Charlie's mother stomped off down the dirt road.

Having Grandma as a buffer gave Charlie a burst of confidence, and even before Grandma's announcement about their partnership, they had become a team. Shortly after Grandma had spoken to him about his new role, Charlie conceived an idea. One day, he noticed how cheap green-broke horses were being sold at the farm auction, and asked Grandma about buying a few young horses, breaking them, and reselling them.

Charlie reminded Grandma that he had riding experience. When he was 6 years old, his dad had given him a black pony named Hitler. Unfortunately, the pony lived up to his name. Hitler threw Charlie every day. He often ran through the barnyard, disrupting his dad's stock, and chased the dogs and kicked at the kids. One summer day he sealed his fate when he tore down a full line of clean clothes and dragged them through the dirt. Esther told Art to take the pony to the auction that day.

Uncle Shorty had left several horses at Grandma's when he went into the service, and Charlie had secretly been riding them when he got a chance. He had found a dusty bridle hanging in the barn and saddle-soaped it into softness. One at a time, he had inched his way onto the horses' backs. Sitting on the broad back of a horse in the silence of the barn, he had many make-believe adventures chasing outlaws and renegade Indians. The idea of owning and riding many horses fired Charlie with excitement.

"Please, Grandma, let me try to do it," he begged. "I know I can do it."

Charlie's Grandma knew that the boy had little time for fun. She figured that if he came out even, the venture would at least have given him something he loved to do.

"Well, OK then," she said. "You can buy two horses and give it a try. We'll see how it goes."

A short time after the purchase of those first two colts, Charlie enlisted the help of the neighborhood boys and girls. Soon, afternoons and early evenings in the corral became a kind of "showdeo" for Charlie and his friends. It started out to be an all-boys club, but when a couple of girls stepped forward and wanted to ride, the boys welcomed them. It quickly grew into a social club.

Grandma, who had raised five boys and five girls, loved having all of the youngsters around. She welcomed them in for meals, offered suggestions when Charlie or one of the other kids had a problem, and bragged on Charlie's "project."

Before very many weeks passed, Charlie could buy the green-broke horses at the sale one week, and within two weeks take them back and ride them in the arena. The reselling of the horses turned into a profitable venture.

At first, Grandma closely supervised the buying, breaking, and selling of the horses. But soon Charlie knew as much or more about handling horses as Grandma. Finally, she began giving Charlie a share of the profits and allowed him to buy and sell at his discretion. She was pleased when Charlie did, in fact, use that money to buy more horses.

Shy Terror

Sometime during those years between ages 9 and 11, Charlie first conceived the idea of becoming a professional jockey. As he mastered the skills of riding, he liked to read anything he could get his hands on about horses and racing. Slowly, he developed a keen interest in Thoroughbred racing and became familiar with famous events like the Kentucky Derby.

At 11, Charlie was tough and athletic, but still small. His wrists and hands were strong from milking, his shoulders muscled from both working on the farm and riding colts. In 1945, when Charlie's Uncle Clarence "Shorty" made it home from World War II, Charlie was an 11-year-old going on 30.

"Charlie, you could be a jockey," Uncle Shorty commented one day.

Charlie's passion for riding and his love of horses took up most of his leisure time by then. He had started to consider the possibility of riding racehorses, but he never had talked about it. He was a partner with Grandma, a farmer and a horseman.

But he and the neighborhood boys often had match-raced two of the horses down the dirt road in front of the farm just for fun. Charlie found that a definite thrill came with outrunning an opponent. That rush of crossing the finish line first always stayed with him long after the race was forgotten. A spark ignited a secret passion inside Charlie. Maybe he really could be a rider. Maybe he would get a chance to actually ride in a real race?

In the meantime, Uncle Shorty rekindled the horse business he had started before going into the Navy. He had acquired a 2-year-old filly named Red Wing, who he asked Charlie to exercise one day.   Charlie had not ridden anything with real speed until he climbed on Red Wing. He had never experienced a horse that pulled at the reins to run. After he breezed the filly down the dirt road in front of the farm, he trotted back with a big grin.

"That's fun," he told his uncle. "When can I ride her in a real race?"

Shorty grinned back and said, "We'll see."

Something about the way he said the words made Charlie sure that his uncle had something brewing.

Shorty Burr was a born gambler. Charlie stood by and watched his uncle bet on everything from footraces to ball games, throwing money to the wind like he had his own personal money tree in the back yard. Charlie suspected that was part of the reason for the heated arguments he had overheard late at night between his uncle and grandmother. Charlie also began to suspect that Shorty's gambling was the reason Grandma had made him a full partner on the farm instead of Shorty.

Several times, Shorty awakened Charlie in the middle of the night to come "read the dice." Shorty and his drinking buddies sometimes stayed up all night, shooting dice in the dimly lit barn. Charlie was brought in to call out the numbers on the dice. The fact that Charlie had to milk the next morning and then attend school mattered little to Shorty, who insisted his nephew remain sometimes for hours on his knees, calling out the numbers.

On several occasions, Shorty helped himself to whatever he wanted on the farm, loading up a cow or pig to sell for money. Although Grandma fussed about the behavior, there had not yet been an all-out confrontation.

Charlie did not like the way Shorty treated Grandma. One day, she begged her son to drive her over to Winfield, Kansas, to help take some cows to a sale there. Shorty had pressing things on his gambling schedule and refused. Charlie had driven around the farm, but of course did not have a driver's license. By then, he was acutely aware that Uncle Shorty resented him being on the farm. A subtle power struggle started to grow between them.

"I'll drive you, Grandma," Charlie boldly said.

Uncle Shorty laughed, "Yeah, why don't you let your partner take you?"

"OK, I will," Grandma proclaimed.

Grandma and Charlie set about ingeniously solving a series of problems. Grandma perched Charlie atop one of her quilts so he could see over the steering wheel, looking like a half-grown bird in a small nest. Blocks of wood were tied to the gas, brake, and clutch pedals so Charlie could reach them with his short legs. Soon, Grandma and Charlie were bumping along the dirt road away from the farm with five cows crammed into the stock racks of the old ton-and-a-half truck bed, bawling their heads off. Grandma proudly navigated from the passenger's seat.

On a warm summer day in 1945, Uncle Shorty loaded Red Wing into a one-horse trailer.

"I'm taking the trailer and truck today," Shorty told Grandma. "I'm takin' Charlie with me, too."

The announcement made Charlie look up from his plate of fried eggs and wait for his grandmother's reply. Shorty could be a pain at times, but life around him was certainly never dull.

Charlie could tell that Grandma's attitude toward Uncle Shorty had hardened over the months. He suspected Grandma's recent bouts of bad temper were directly related to Shorty's gambling. Grandma was not going to let anyone, including her own son, run over her. Shorty's tendency to sell things off so he could get fresh money for gambling was about to reach a limit with Grandma.

"I told you, Shorty, I've made Charlie a partner," Grandma said. "He's helped me keep things going all the time you were gone. You can't come back here and sell off the cows and horses one at a time."

"Don't get your hackles up, Mom, I'm not selling anything today," Shorty replied. "I'm just taking the trailer and going down to the races."

Grandma hesitated and looked from her son to her grandson, considering the situation.

"OK. You take Charlie with you," Grandma said. "Let him ride your horse."

Charlie put his fork down and stared. Was he actually going to ride in a real race?

He wanted to ask, but before he could open his mouth, Grandma looked straight at him. "You mind yourself, you hear?"

Then she turned, squinted eyed, back to Shorty.

"If you take that boy off and get him hurt, you will answer to me, Clarence," she declared, using Shorty's real name.

The next thing he knew, Charlie found himself bumping along in the old pickup truck, traveling south across the state line toward nearby Ponca City, Oklahoma.

Once at the track, Uncle Shorty lifted Charlie into the saddle, pointed him toward the gate, and walked off. He had betting to do. Charlie had never ridden a horse into a starting gate before, so he paid little attention to anything except the rider next to him. He watched how the other rider approached, how he talked to the horse to inch him into the narrow chute, and how he got himself positioned. He watched the way the jockey sat in the saddle and the way he held his reins. Charlie's heart rattled so loud he wondered if the other rider could hear it.

Charlie waited for the gate to open, trying to remember to breathe. He thought about all of those green colts and how many times he had hit the dirt. Red Wing could be temperamental. She had bolted the track with him at home once, and another time she had run a short distance and then stopped abruptly, nearly tossing Charlie over her head.

In the distance, Charlie could see men lining up along the finish line, could hear the crowd grow silent. He was not afraid of getting hurt, but it would be embarrassing if the horse ran off with him or he got thrown. He never had raced a horse with an audience.

Bang! The gates opened and Red Wing lunged forward so quickly that Charlie's butt came up and out of the saddle. He managed to hold onto the reins and leaned forward, urging the mare on. To his delight, Red Wing finished well ahead of the other horse.

As suddenly as the race began, it was over. Charlie had won his first race riding Red Wing that day in 1945 at the Ponca City Bush Track. The applause and shouts from the crowd warmed Charlie's ears as he rode Red Wing back down the track. Uncle Shorty slapped Charlie on the shoulder and grabbed the bridle reins.

"Good job, boy," he exclaimed.

Charlie became a jockey before he even had time to really understand what had happened. Being first across the finish line, standing up in the saddle and waving to the cheering crowd, sent his heart soaring. And at the end of the day, he had money jingling in his pockets. The combination of those two things, the thrill and the money, hooked young Charlie. Circumstances hurled him forward.

Back in those active days of bush track racing, owners and trainers were always on the lookout for fresh talent. The minute a young rider won a race, he was immediately in demand. Charlie received a phone call just days after his race in Ponca City.

A man named Clifford Brown wanted to come get Charlie the next weekend and take him to Pond Creek, Oklahoma, to ride a horse named Buttons. That was the beginning of a series of events that set Charlie's destiny in motion.

One Friday, a local man named Paul Allen and his little rider, Jimmy Stockton, came to Charlie's school to get Charlie to ride some match races on the dirt track in Arkansas City. Even though the teacher complained loudly, the men escorted Charlie down the hall and out of the building. Before long, getting pulled out of school on Friday was a weekly occurrence in Charlie's life.

Because Fridays were test days at school and Charlie seemed to have little say about his frequent absences, all six of his teachers finally accepted the fact that something had to be done, and one came up with a practical solution. Each of them could start giving tests to Charlie on Thursdays in an attempt to keep him from failing.

By the time he entered eighth grade, it had become a known fact that Charlie's test day was Thursday instead of Friday. Whatever failings the school system may have had during that time, Charlie always appreciated the fact that his teachers did all they could to keep him in school.

At the age of 13, Charlie won on My Chocolate in Springfield, Missouri.

At age 13, Charlie's summer life revolved around the local bush tracks. The circuit that Charlie rode included Newkirk, Pond Creek, Enid, Pawhuska, and Temple, Oklahoma; Wichita, Kansas; Springfield, Missouri; and Brady, Texas. Charlie's reputation as a rider slowly spread.

Work on the farm still came first during the week, but usually an owner, trainer, or rider would arrive early Friday morning to haul Charlie off for the entire weekend. At times, Uncle Shorty would drive Charlie to a meet and stay with him. Other times, his dad would take him. Soon, Charlie was driving himself, without a license.

Grandma fussed and sometimes ranted about the fact that her partner was abandoning her, but she supported Charlie's new goal to "become the best jockey racing had ever seen." She attended the races when she could to cheer Charlie on.

Slowly, Grandma resigned herself to the fact that the farm, with all of the cows, pigs, and chickens, had become too much for both her and Charlie, so she began to entertain the idea of giving the property to her grandson and building a small house down the street to retire in.

In the summer of 1948, at age 14, Charlie weighed 84 pounds and stood 5'3" tall. His life completely entangled in the racetrack, Charlie's territory had expanded from the Oklahoma bush tracks to weekend fair meets in four neighboring states. Sometimes Charlie smiled to himself when he remembered thinking he had become a man on Grandma's farm at 9 years old. Since he had turned 11 and ventured out into the bigger world, he realized how naïve he had been.

In three years, Charlie had learned a lot about horses and people. He had seen the good, the bad, and the ugly. He had experienced terrible abuse by some of the owner/trainers, but had also met good men who took time to graciously teach him. One day, his uncle had tossed him in the back of a pickup after an injury at Pond Creek, Oklahoma, and there he lay with a concussion in the hot sun, unnoticed for hours. He was rescued by a total stranger from Ponca City who drove him all the way home.

Bloodied, kicked, bitten, and banged by the rogues, Charlie still fell in love with some of the best Quarter Horses in Oklahoma, the ponies that had big hearts and loved to run as much as he loved to ride. From Kansas to Texas to Missouri, Charlie began to realize that his journey into manhood had just begun.

Caught up now in the glory of crossing that wire, Charlie stumbled forward with what some would later describe as a crazed indifference. He would succeed no matter what the cost. He would ride anything and ride it well. He would make a ton of money and one day own a large horse operation of his own.

In August, 1948 Charlie won a 5-furlong race on Fairy Fawn in Springfield, Missouri at the age of 14.

Charlie had become the "shy terror." Quiet and shy around people, he became a terror the moment he put one foot in a stirrup. He was in the race for one reason, to win. At 9 years old, Grandma taught him that any job worth starting was worth finishing. If he had to bump, flip a rider's foot from the stirrup, or bully him with words, Charlie was determined to win.

By then, Charlie had told his father, "I'm going to win three Kentucky Derbys in a row, like Eddie Arcaro did."

Shortly after he said those words, Charlie won all 14 races at a meet in Fairfax, Oklahoma.

The day after the Fairfax meet, Uncle Shorty told his brother, "That boy of yours may go all the way."

Art knew better than anyone that his son was strong and stubborn. When Charlie made the statement about riding like Eddie Arcaro, Art did not repeat the brag. But he did not doubt the possibility, either. Even Charlie's mother began to take a new interest in her oldest son's accomplishments. Charlie's cheering section grew. His parents, siblings, and a large group of followers from Arkansas City now joined Grandma, who had been a fan from day one.

By then, listening to the men set up the weekend match races around the track was all too familiar to Charlie. He came to ride. Until all of the talk was finished, he did not have a paying job.

"I've got a little mare that can run like hell for 200 yards. What did you bring today?" one owner would say.

After a pause and careful contemplation someone would step up, "That little bay gelding of mine can outrun her for 220."

"I've got 20 that says she can't."

"Make it 50 and you have yourself a horse race."

And so it would begin. Sometimes the bantering would go on for hours before the match races actually began. Usually the first two or three hours at the track were a time for Charlie to just hang out. Maybe he would help friends with various chores at the barn, but more often than not he would read a comic book or find someone to talk to.

At Chisholm Trail Park in Pond Creek in 1949, Charlie won on Aunt Annie owned by E.A. Carter.

Charlie won in Enid August 11, 1950 on Little Peppy owned by Bill Sharp, running 300 yards in 16.5.

One windy Oklahoma day in late summer, he sat in a ditch at the Enid bush track and shot dice for several hours with another rider while they waited for the races to begin. Bobby Baker, as he was known back then, was one of the first boys Charlie had met in the bushes. Bobby was tough and he was not afraid of anything. Bobby later used the name Bobby Ussery, Charlie respected Bobby and competed against him many times from 1948 through 1950. Both boys had big dreams that they sometimes talked about, but neither knew back in that ditch in 1949 that they would one day compete from New Jersey to New York and back.

Another rider who would compete against Charlie time after time was a skinny kid two years younger than him from Ponca City, Oklahoma, Clayton Epperson. "Little Epp," as they called him around the track, was also a tough competitor. He had started riding at 9 years old, and by the time Charlie met him at a match race in Newkirk, Oklahoma, 13-year-old Clayton was a force to be reckoned with.

To the unschooled eye, the win picture taken in June 1949 at the Newkirk Race Track showed only one horse in the race. Clayton on Trigger and Charlie riding Snip were running so close it appeared that a lone horse was crossing the finish line. That win picture, in many ways, characterized the closeness of a friendship that would last a lifetime.

Because Charlie won by a "whisker," he was a smart aleck when the results were finally announced. "Where were you, boy?" he asked Clayton.

In the rain at Chisholm Trail Park in April, 1950, Charlie won on Zasta owned by H. Murphy.

Clayton's laughter boomed out spontaneously.

Charlie was impressed not only with Clayton's skill, but his sportsmanship. He was not sure he would have laughed if he had lost. Clayton was impressed with Charlie's confidence. The mutual attraction instantly clicked and over the next few years, as the two grew up in the bushes, the friendship also grew.

The boys' experience on the Oklahoma bush track circuit gave them common ground. Only another rider could understand what life on the circuit entailed. By the time Charlie was 14 and Clayton 12, they had ridden the same horses, knew the same trainers and owners, and suffered many of the same accidents.

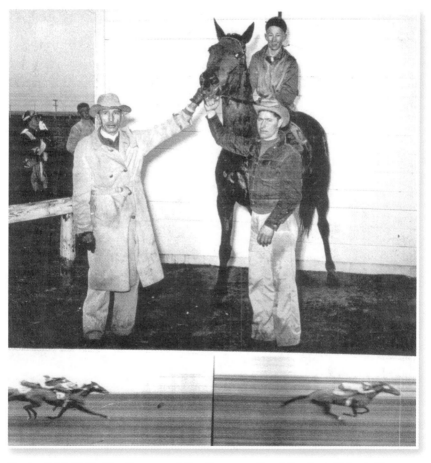

On April 16, 1950, Charlie won a 5/8 mile race at Pond Creek on Take A Chance owned by Vance Stowers.

Charlie on Oklahoma Loa.

If you were not tough, you would not be riding horses on the bush tracks for long. One owner had a reputation for having his horses raise hell in the gate. He was famous for his hose technique. The owner would push his horse into the gate with his shoulder and when the gate opened, he would slap the horse hard on the rump with a rubber hose. Of course those horses always were nervous in the gate.

One day, one of the man's horses started acting up and threw Charlie into the gate. Charlie barely remembered waking up under the horse and getting pulled out and slapped back up on the horse's back. He was still woozy when the race was over. The owner jumped him and told him what a bad race he had ridden.

Charlie and Clayton had secret names for some of the trainers and owners, names that could not be repeated to others. If they had a choice, they would not ride for a man who mistreated his horses, but oftentimes they did not have a choice. Instead, they learned to never shy away from fear. When they climbed up on a horse with a name like "Hell's a Poppin," they learned to be prepared for almost anything. The horse might flip in the gate, run away, or bite. It did little good for the riders to ask a question like "Can this horse handle the turn?" because they knew the answer before they asked: "Oh, he handles that turn like a rat around a barrel." Which probably meant that the horse would blast to the outside and right through the rail.

Being mistreated by strangers was only part of the equation for the young riders. Often, family members would also take advantage of their youth and inexperience. One Sunday, Uncle Shorty took Charlie to the track in Ponca City. Charlie rode 17 horses that day. After the races, he started looking for Shorty so he could get his money and go home. He could not find his uncle. Charlie did not get paid for one ride that day, and he was alone on the track without a way home. He started walking and a man at a nearby house asked him what he was doing. When Charlie explained, the man called Charlie's dad. Art drove down to get his oldest son.

Charlie and Clayton learned early on to keep their mouths shut and ride. Back in those days, kids did not talk back to the adults around them. And oftentimes, although they saw trouble coming, they did not speak a word. That early training, to work hard, do what they were told and ride, would later serve them well.

Charlie's independence evolved from his being in so many situations where he was forced to take care of himself. Courage and perseverance determined which riders made it from the rural bush tracks to the Big Apple.

At 14, Charlie Burr was not afraid of much and there was no "give up" in him. Although a lot of what he saw around the track made him want to lose faith in human nature, someone always mysteriously appeared in his life when he needed help. For example, one night Charlie was sleeping in the front seat of a car on the way back from a meet in Pond Creek. Another rider was driving. Charlie awoke to the words, "You better wake up and hold on."

Charlie sat up and looked out at a solid sheet of rain and felt the car sliding backwards. They slid into a water-filled ravine and had to abandon the car. Exhausted from riding at the three-day meet, Charlie and the rider stood out on the road in the rain at 3 in the morning. A forlorn feeling of defeat washed over Charlie, and he asked himself if he was sure the jockey life was what he really wanted.

Just as he had that thought, Charlie saw a car coming down the highway in the rain. The car passed them, stopped, and backed up. A man, his wife, and three little kids were in the car.

"What happened to you boys?" the man asked.

Charlie explained and the man told them to get in. He took them to town, paid for a motel room, and left before Charlie could get his name.

In 1949, Grandma followed through on her plan to build a small house and turn the farm over to Charlie, when he was almost 15. Charlie let his parents move into the farmhouse to help him take care of the few cows, pigs, and chickens that were still on the farm. When he was home from riding on the circuit, he stayed sometimes on his farm with his parents and sometimes with Grandma.

Charlie brought home most of his money to help his family and invest in the farm. He continued to struggle through high school in between race meets.

At the first of three meets at Chisholm Trail Park in Pond Creek in 1949, Charlie opened his season on the Oklahoma-Kansas racing circuit by riding home three firsts, a second, and a third in five races.

Before a crowd of more than 1,000 spectators, 15-year-old Charlie romped home in the five-eighths-mile heat on Take-A-Chance in 65.2 seconds. He rode Mary's Fairy in the second race and sliced off two seconds from the previous time. His third win was on Sooner in another five-eighths-mile race.

Later that same summer, at Garfield Race Track in Enid, a trainer named Pete Maxwell approached Charlie. Pete told Charlie that he trained horses out near St. Louis, at Fairmont Park in Collinsville, Illinois. He expressed an interest in having Charlie come ride for him the minute he turned 16.

Charlie Burr at 16.

"You have a lot of talent, son," Pete said. "I'd like to have you on my team. You could break your maiden at Fairmont Park."

Charlie liked Pete and knew he had been given an opportunity. He started counting the days until his 16th birthday, when he would be old enough to travel out of state and ride on the sanctioned tracks. Fairmont Park would be only the beginning. Charlie had bigger things in mind.

For more than a year, Charlie had ridden horses for James Reese at the meets in Enid and Pond Creek. Not too long after he started riding Reese's horses, he began

Charlie in a win picture on James Reese Ranch.

dating his daughter, Norma Jean. Friendship and trust gradually developed between James and Charlie, and one day James offered Charlie a job on his ranch in Temple, Oklahoma, for the summer. James had a small house behind his ranch house where Charlie could live. He also had a straightaway track right on his ranch. When he went to the three-day meets, Charlie would ride James Reese's horses first, and then any other horses he wanted to ride. James would pay him a regular salary and give him room and board for helping him with the horses at his ranch. Charlie could sharpen his riding skills on the nearby track, learn more about the training process and get paid while he was doing it.

KANSAS BOY CHAMPION JOCKEY

CHILDHOOD SWEETHEARTS—Charlie Burr and 17-year-old Jean Reece of Temple, Ok., have talked about getting married. Charlie met Jean while riding the race horses of her father, James Reece, an oil man.

Old newspaper picture of Charlie and his sweetheart, Jean Reece, in a Kansas newspaper after Charlie left Kansas and began riding his way toward leading rider of the nation.

The offer seemed to be a win-win situation. He was fond of Norma Jean and he could learn a lot from Reese. The minute school let out for the summer, Charlie packed his few belongings, left his parents in charge of the farm, kissed Grandma good-bye, and moved 200 miles south of Arkansas City to Temple.

For the next few months, Charlie rode James's horses every day. On the weekends, he accompanied James to three-day meets in Oklahoma and Texas. Charlie and Norma Jean spent most of their leisure time together.

Charlie rode some great horses during his bush track years, but his favorites were Fairfax Leo, Ponca Blue, and Kanzo. When he started riding for James Reese, Charlie fell in love with three of his horses, Gray Lady, Lady Gray, and Flicka F.

The week Charlie turned 16, in May 1950, his parents came to southern Oklahoma to watch him ride at a race meet on James' ranch. After the meet, James invited Charlie and his parents to come sit and talk in his car.

Charlie sat in the front seat next to Norma Jean and listened as James made him an offer.

"I know you and Norma Jean are getting serious, Charlie," he said. "I've done a lot of thinking and I want to make you an offer, son. If you marry my daughter, I'll give you interest in several of my oil wells, guarantee you an education, and eventually make you a partner."

Charlie's dad spoke up from the back seat.

"Charlie, that's a fine offer, son," he said. "I want you to get an education."

"You need to think of what's best for your future," Charlie's mother added.

Charlie felt trapped. He squirmed in the seat and glanced at Norma Jean. He was very fond of his girlfriend, but his riding came before anything. He knew nothing about oil wells or marriage. Everyone was staring at him, waiting for him to say something. It seemed as though his entire future had to be decided in that second.

"I'm sorry," he said, stumbling out of the car. "I can't make that decision right now."

Charlie's father and mother were mad at him and tried late into the night to make him reconsider. Charlie called his Grandma in Arkansas City.

"Grandma, I'm all mixed up," he said. "I don't know what to do."

After only a brief hesitation, the familiar voice sounded clearly through the receiver, "When a person is confused like that, it's always best to give it some time."

Charlie took Grandma's advice, but for the next four months time seemed like a revolving door of questions he could not answer. James continued to pressure him, sweetening the offer almost every week. Norma Jean had emotional outbursts that jerked Charlie back and forth. Art and Esther called often and wrote several letters pressuring Charlie to accept the offer.

Then Pete Maxwell called Charlie shortly after he turned 16 and again offered him a contract to ride in Collinsville, at Fairmont Park.

The pressure mounted into a tornado of confusion that consumed Charlie from May until early September. Then, one bright morning after a torrential Oklahoma rain, Charlie awoke knowing exactly what he had to do. It amazed him that the answer to his dilemma had been there from the beginning, but until that day he had not been able to clearly see it.

His dream for quite awhile had been to ride on the East Coast. He had to give it a try. For five long years he had paid his dues on the bush tracks of Oklahoma and neighboring states. He had slept on the ground at three-day meets, ate only one meal a day to get by, and worked from daylight until dark while trying to remain in school. At times, he had survived on pure adrenalin.

It was his dream to ride in the Big Apple that got him past all of the hundreds of bad horses, ignorant owners, and humiliations along the way.

The security of James Reese's offer, the thought of marriage to Norma Jean, and an easy life on the ranch were all temptations that made his belly hurt. But now he understood the four months of turmoil. The shy terror had been at war with himself. The shy, lazy part of him yearned to accept the offer, to nestle into a secure existence, and live happily ever after. But the restless terror had screamed "NO" from the first day. The passionate part of him that loved the independent life of the circuit, the soul part of him that lived for the thrill of racing, knew that neither love nor the security of money would ever completely satisfy him if he gave up his dream.

This Boy is No Apprentice

Charlie called Pete Maxwell on September 6, 1950.

"Mr. Maxwell," he said, "I want to come ride for you if you still want me."

"Can you be back home in Arkansas City tomorrow?" Pete asked.

"I'll be there."

"Your parents will have to sign the papers with you."

"They will."

Two days later, Pete picked Charlie up at the farm. Art and Esther Burr begrudgingly signed the contract, allowing Charlie to ride for Pete, but still telling him they thought he should take James Reece's offer, instead.

Grandma hugged Charlie before he climbed into Pete's car.

"I'm proud of you for listening to your heart," she told him.

For a moment, Charlie longed for things past. He wanted to be 9 years old again and go back in the house with Grandma. He knew he was really leaving home, this time for good. No matter what happened or how long he stayed away, life on the farm with Grandma was gone forever. As if she read his thoughts, Grandma smiled.

"You know where home is, Charles," she said. "No matter what happens, you can always come home to your old grandma."

Pete and Charlie drove all night. They pulled into Fairmont Park in Collinsville, Illinois, the next day. Pete had Charlie scheduled to ride six horses that evening, and late in the afternoon, before the races, a valet approached Charlie.

"Where's your saddle?" the valet asked.

"I don't have my own saddle," Charlie replied, embarrassed.

The valets must have felt sorry for the little bush track rider that Pete Maxwell had brought in from some farm in Kansas. They chipped in and together bought Charlie a used saddle.

Charlie quickly learned that the valets each handled two or three riders. A valet's job was to pick out the jockey's colors for the races of the day, polish his boots and saddle, and have all of the equipment in top shape.

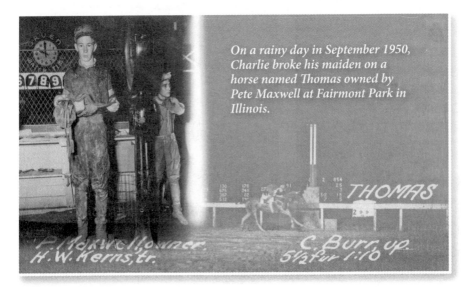

On a rainy day in September 1950, Charlie broke his maiden on a horse named Thomas owned by Pete Maxwell at Fairmont Park in Illinois.

Charlie on Hunter's Pride at Fairmont Park.

Charlie thanked the valets over and over for the saddle. Not only did he now have a saddle of his own, he had someone waiting on him, treating him like royalty. Life on the sanctioned tracks was going to be everything he had imagined.

But before the first night of racing was finished, Charlie realized there would be good and bad. Charlie won on Thomas in the first race, and then came right back and won on Jennie Weaver. A racing steward quickly extinguished the spark of glory from Charlie's back-to-back wins.

"This boy is no apprentice," the steward grumbled, and then he proceeded to try to take Charlie's license.

Of course they could not do that, because Charlie truly was an apprentice, a "bug boy" who had just broken his maiden in the first race at Fairmont Park. Pete Maxwell came to the rescue. Under racing law at that time, apprentice bug boys were given a five-pound weight allowance for a year or until they rode 40 winners under the wire.

"I picked this boy up yesterday on a farm in Kansas," Pete said. "He's ridden since he was 9 in the bushes. He's never ridden on a sanctioned track until today."

Charlie on Ginny Weaver at Fairmont Park.

The grumbling steward respected Pete and took his word, but remained doubtful. A boy from the bush tracks coming in and winning his first two races? That was one for the record books!

Charlie Burr rode six days at Fairmont Park and won 14 races. Things seemed to be going great, but then, with no explanation, Pete mysteriously grabbed him up and took him to Beulah Park in Columbus, Ohio.

What Charlie did not know was that Robert Dienst, the owner of Beulah Park, wanted to see this 16-year-old Charles Burr from the bushes, who had come in and won 14 races in six days at Fairmont Park. That kind of performance was unbelievable.

Dienst asked Pete to take Charlie to Hawthorn Park and let the young Kansas jockey ride the last part of that meet for his trainer, Mr. Shepp. Charlie won several races at Hawthorn, and then went next door with Shepp to Sportsman's Park in Chicago. It was a stroke of sheer luck for Charlie that Sportsman's Park was a half-mile bullring track. Charlie had grown up riding on half-mile bullrings.

Charlie became leading rider at the 30-day meet at Sportsman's Park. Dienst immediately bought his contract from Pete. Charlie agreed to a three-year contract to ride for River Divide Farms in October 1950, one month after he left home. The official contract, dated February 26, 1951, was signed by Robert Dienst, Charlie, as a minor, and Arthur and Esther Burr. The contract commenced on September 8, 1950, and would expire on September 8, 1953. The age of said minor was 16 years, 3 months, and 23 days. The contract stated: "The nature of the service for which the said minor is bound is that of stable boy and rider. . . ."

One day, toward the end of the meet at Sportsman's Park, Shepp told Charlie to gallop a horse. Charlie took the horse out on the track and breezed him, then went back to the barn. There, Shepp became upset. He made Charlie quit riding and start cooling horses. Charlie was not sure why he was being punished. In the bushes, all Charlie had ever done was ride in races or breeze a horse down to the half-mile, so that is all he knew.

As Charlie walked horses instead of riding that day, he tried to think of a way to explain to Shepp why he had made the mistake. But Shepp stayed busy near the track and Charlie did not approach him. Shepp was a tough man, all business.

Charlie later tried to explain to the exercise boys that he had never galloped a horse. The boys stared at him in disbelief, like he was trying to put something over on them. How could a boy who had just become leading rider at the 30-day meet at Sportsman's Park not know how to gallop a horse?

After several futile attempts to get information from the exercise boys about galloping, Charlie gave up. He would learn by watching and listening. It was impossible to make anyone understand how he had learned to ride on the bush tracks—the way Uncle Shorty had thrown him up on Redwing and walked away. Charlie was beginning to really understand how little he knew. There was a big difference between the racing Quarter Horses he had grown up with and the world of Thoroughbred racing.

In December, just three months after Charlie left home, he went with Shepp to Hialeah Race Track in Hialeah, Florida. Trainers and owners back then did not usually take care of little bug boys from the bush track, no matter how promising they might be. No one offered Charlie a room or a suggestion of where to stay. No one told him how to eat until he drew his first pay. No one took him by the hand and guided him through what was expected on the track.

But Charlie was used to hard work and he had made many adjustments in his 16 years. He slowly began to settle into his new surroundings and find his way.

Shepp demanded perfection from the men who worked for him. Two of the exercise boys got fired within that first week in Florida. The third, an older, more experienced rider, began to teach Charlie what it meant to gallop a horse. He made him realize that each horse was an individual, with an individual personality and individual workouts. Charlie listened attentively and learned by riding.

After a few weeks in Florida, Charlie had a much better grasp on what was expected of him. He had settled into a small apartment across from the track on Palm Avenue, figured out how to stretch his money at the grocery store, and cook a meal. He knew how to gallop a horse and how to always listen carefully to every word of the instructions from Shepp.

Charlie loved Florida. When he would talk to his folks back in Kansas or Norma Jean, they would tell him about the harsh winter. Charlie vividly remembered the cold Kansas wind slamming him in the face each morning when he would get up before daylight to milk. He remembered the icy dampness that crawled beneath his coat and sent shivers up his back. It seemed strange, but wonderful, to wake up every morning in December to bright sunshine. Charlie marveled at the flowers growing in profusion around the track.

One brilliant morning in early January, Charlie rode a filly down the path toward the track to gallop her. A beautiful, splashing fountain sat at the edge of the track, where the path ended. The sound or sight of the fountain scared the filly, and she balked and would not go onto the track. Charlie talked to her, turned her back, walked her up several times, but she seemed terrified of the fountain and simply would not go onto the track.

After several futile attempts, Charlie ran out of ideas. He rode the filly as close to the fountain as he could get her and made her stand a few minutes, then he turned her and took her back to the barn. Charlie always had found it easier to go gently with a young horse, gain their trust. He did not believe in forcing the issue.

Shepp happened to be standing right by the barn watching him, and asked Charlie why he had not worked the filly.

"I couldn't get her to go past the fountain, sir," Charlie replied, frustrated.

Shepp did not say a word, but the first thing the next morning, he sent Charlie out on the same filly. Charlie rode the filly down the path, wondering what he was going to do to get her past the fountain. He had no idea Shepp was walking behind him, carrying a five-foot bullwhip.

Just as Charlie reached the fountain and the filly balked, Shepp hit her and Charlie with the whip. Charlie almost jumped out of the saddle as the filly leaped onto the track running. Managing to get his seat back in the saddle and get a good hold on the reins, Charlie tried to control the filly, but it was too late. A trainer named Ben Jones, who worked for Calumet Farms, was walking a string of horses onto the track. Charlie and the filly burst through the string, disrupting possibly the best string of horses in America at that time. Jones was fighting mad and stomped over to Shepp.

"That rider of yours . . . ," he yelled.

Shepp held up his hand and said, "I did it. Don't blame the boy. That filly balked at the fountain and I popped her with the bullwhip."

He then turned to Charlie and introduced him to Jones. In that moment, Charlie's respect for Shepp grew. He realized that although the trainer was tough, he also was fair.

Charlie never forgot the incident. It made him realize that even the bad experiences he had along the way could hold the possibility of promise. He ended up riding many horses for Calumet Farms. That opportunity probably would not have presented itself if he had not burst out onto the track that morning, at that particular moment, and disrupted Ben Jones' horses.

When the meet in Hialeah ended, Charlie went with Shepp to Gulf Stream Park in Hallandale. He continued to be first under the wire, mounting up incredible win records that would soon make him leading apprentice rider of 1951. But in April his win streak came to a screeching halt.

Charlie was riding into the turn at Gulf Stream when three horses went down in front of him. The experience was surreal for Charlie, who by then felt himself invincible. One moment he was concentrating on where to position his horse when they approached the turn, and the next, three horses piled up directly in his path. Charlie took a bad spill that banged him up and broke his left wrist.

It took only three seconds for the accident to unfold, but it played out in Charlie's memory in slow motion for years to come. Unbelievably, it never shook his confidence. Instead, it made him appreciate the fact that each day in the irons was a gift.

There was no place for an injured rider around the track, so Shepp sent Charlie to Arkansas City to heal, with strict instructions to rest. Charlie returned home somewhat of a celebrity. His brothers and the neighborhood kids bombarded him with questions.

"What was it like in Fairmont Park? What did it feel like to win that first race? What was it like in Florida? Where would he go when he healed?"

Charlie enjoyed the limelight, as would any typical 16-year-old. He basked in all of the attention he received from Grandma and especially appreciated the home-cooked meals. He sat out on the old porch at Grandma's in the afternoons with his comic books around him, telling stories about Chicago and Florida to several eager listeners.

Charlie drove down to Ponca City one day to look up his friend Clayton Epperson. He knew by then that the meet in Florida had ended, and when the cast came off he would be driving back to the East Coast to continue his contract with Robert Dienst.

Charlie diligently had saved his money and decided to buy a new car. It would be great fun to have his bush track buddy with him. He would impress his young friend and let Lil Epp know what could be ahead for him.

Clayton had no way of knowing that Charlie actually was going to buy a car that day, and Charlie reveled in every moment of "big dogging it" that afternoon as Clayton followed him around the showroom floor of the car dealership in Ponca City. He asked the salesman one question after another about the shining Rocket 88 Oldsmobile while his younger buddy watched. Then, when Charlie said, "I think I'll take her," he delighted in the look of shock on 15-year-old Clayton's face.

As they wheeled out of the dealership onto Grand Avenue that afternoon, Charlie grinned and told Clayton, "Keep riding, buddy. This time next year, you'll be buying yourself a brand new car."

Shepp called every few days to check on Charlie's progress, and after six weeks, when the doctor in Arkansas City released him to ride, Charlie called Shepp. The meet in Florida had ended and Shepp was back on the East Coast tracks. Charlie packed his bags into his new Oldsmobile and left for Boston.

Charlie's glory days had begun. From Massachusetts to New Hampshire to Rhode Island, Charles Burr took the East Coast tracks by storm, racking up a record number of wins along the way.

After Charlie fulfilled his contract obligation to ride for Dienst and River Divide Farms, he could accept other mounts. He soon had an agent, John McQuade, to book those engagements for him. Charlie got the standard $20 for each mount he accepted to ride. He was often paid $35 for finishing second and $50 for winning, though the scale varied at tracks across the country. Many owners of winning horses paid the jockey 10 percent of the winnings instead of the $50.

Charlie had no idea from week to week what he might make, but he soon found out that the money was substantially better than what he had made on the bush tracks just one year before. In the bushes, Charlie usually got paid $5 to ride a horse, and rarely made more than $10. He seldom saw a bonus for riding winners and often-

Charlie, left, and Joe Culmone with a list of jockeys with 300 or more wins. By November 1951, one year after he left home for Fairmont Park, the young man from the bushes was Leading Rider of the Nation in number of race victories.

times would not get paid at all. He had gone from that to winning as much as $15,000 for a two-minute ride in a big stakes race.

By the end of 1951, Charlie was forwarding home as much as $1,500 a week to his parents to deposit in the bank for his new dream, a horse-breeding farm.

At age 17, Charlie stood 5' 3" tall and weighed 103 pounds. His spindly frame and freckled face would have deceived an unknowing bystander into believing the youth was just another boy. But by November 1951, one year after leaving home for Fairmont Park, the young man from the bushes was the leading rider in the nation in the number of race victories.

Charlie suddenly found himself in the company of racing legends. Joseph Culmone and Willie Shoemaker tied for leading rider in 1950, each having 388 wins to his credit. By the amount of money won, Shoemaker, Eddie Arcaro, and Ted Atkinson were the top three jockeys in 1951, and Charlie was already in the top 10 on that list.

At the end of 1951, Charlie became the second-youngest reins man in the history of the sport to pass the 300-win mark in a single year. Charlie took the national championship with 310 wins and a 24 percent success record at the age of 17. Jack Westrope was 16 when he won the honor in 1934, the same year Charlie was born.

In the November, 1951 Kansas City Star writer Robert Kelley said it well: "Charlie Burr hasn't got the accurate sense of timing that makes Eddie Arcaro almost machine-like in the saddle, or the hustle of Steve Brooks in getting a horse out of the starting gate. He certainly hasn't the polish of Earl Sande—at least not yet. But he has got an ever-increasing amount of all those qualities, plus a cold-blooded fearlessness that is belied by his innocent, choir-boy face."

In an article from *TIME* Magazine, the writer described 17-year-old Charlie Burr thusly: "Charlie is a shy little fellow with a guileless grin; on a horse, he is a hot-tempered terror. This year he got a nine-day suspension for slashing a jockey, got another 10 days for causing a spill, was fined $200 for cussing out another rider, and was out of action for 48 days with a broken wrist after a three-horse pileup."

Charlie was riding high by the end of that year, officially known by all as "Leading Rider of the Nation." He had become the seventh jockey ever to win 300 or more races in one season. And, amazingly, he had accomplished the feat in less than 10 months as he had not raced for 75 days during his recuperation from the broken wrist and his suspensions.

Newspaper reporters from Arkansas City to Boston had a field day with the success story of the young man from the Kansas farm who had learned to ride on bush tracks. Charlie had his picture taken with such notables as Sugar Ray Robinson and famed woman golfer and athlete Babe Didrikson Zaharias. Charlie earned the New England Turf Writer's award "for outstanding contribution to New England racing." His weekly income had risen to $60,000. He bought himself a new Packard and sent large sums of money home to his dad for his future horse ranch.

But in the article for *TIME* Magazine, the writer mentioned that when he ap-

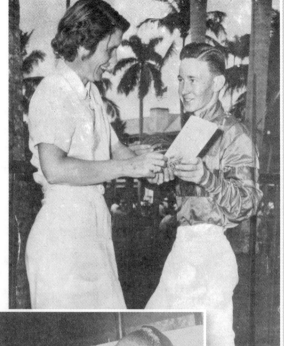

Charlie with famed woman golfer Babe Didrikson Zaharias.

By the end of 1951, Charlie was riding high as leading rider of the nation. He had his picture taken with many recognized personalities, including Sugar Ray Robinson.

proached Charlie to do the interview, the young jockey was reading a comic book. It was a mixture of Charlie's immaturity, his independence, and his lack of a mentor to guide him that shaped his destiny after his rise to fame in 1951. He loved to ride, but almost from the beginning of his success, Charlie longed for home. The homesickness plagued him so much in those early years that he would return home for a few days so he could "snap out of it."

Very soon after Charlie's success, he began to get resentful over the fact that he was controlled by other people. At 16, his parents and Reese had put him under a tremendous amount of pressure to "do what was best." Even after he stepped out of that situation and made his own decision, it was his parents who had signed the legal contract for him to ride for Pete Maxwell. Then, in Chicago, when Dienst wanted to buy Charlie's contract from Pete Maxwell, Dienst dealt with Charlie's parents again.

Suspended from riding on sanctioned tracks back east in 1952, Charlie returned to the bushes. In the win circle on a horse from Oklahoma with Joe Neff, from Fairfax, holding the horse.

Charlie's younger brother, Joe Burr won on Kay County Bill in a match race on June 25, 1952 with Joe Neff holding horse, Grandma Burr, and Charlie's dad, Art Burr at Newkirk. It was common for the younger brother to step up when the older brother left for the Big Apple. COURTESY HOLTON PAYNE.

All of those hard years of being on his own, the years that got him where he wanted to be, had become a double-edged sword. Charlie became bitter. Why was everyone able to make decisions about his life but him?

Another frustration that was common among jockeys at that time became a sore spot for Charlie. If a jockey got an opportunity to ride a great horse in one of the big races, like the Kentucky Derby, but the jockey was under contract to a certain farm and that farm had a horse running, the jockey had to ride for his contract owner.

Charlie's resentments erupted in a dispute with Dienst in 1952 in Florida. His boss wanted him to go back to New Jersey from Florida, but Charlie wanted to go to Boston. They had a falling out and Dienst had Charlie set down. Charlie suddenly could not ride anywhere because he had disagreed with his owner.

Charlie was livid. The big boys on the block could come along and buy little bug boys for a minimum lump sum, treat them like a stepchild, and work them into the ground. Every time Charlie crawled onto a horse, his life was at risk. He had no IRA, no real future security of any kind, and very little say in major decisions that affected his own life. Thanks to the Jockey's Guild he did have limited health insurance, but like every rider alive, he knew that would not go far enough in the event of a major injury.

Charlie probably never had heard the saying, "You can't fight City Hall." Even if he had, he probably would not have listened. Charlie was a born pioneer. He was the first of many jockeys to stand up for his rights as a human being.

The Leading Rider of the Nation in 1951 did not get to ride for five months in 1952. In order to ride again, he had only one choice—he had to buy his contract back from Dienst. Charlie ended up paying a lawyer $750 and paid $8,000 for his contract. Eight thousand dollars was a fortune to the average person in 1952.

Charlie was a survivor. While he was under contract they might own him on the sanctioned tracks, but they could not keep him from riding. He returned to Arkansas City and to the Oklahoma bush tracks doing what he loved to do.

That summer of 1952, Charlie claimed victories on the bush tracks from Newkirk to Burden, Kansas, to as far away as Yuma, Colorado. The shy terror had just begun. He would return to the Big Apple. He would continue his dream. They would not beat him.

Burr in the Saddle

The years between 1952 and 1954 were rocky ones for young Charlie. After five hectic months of legal entanglements and being banned from racing, he finally was released from his contract with Robert Dienst. The moment Charlie could legally crawl back in the irons, he left Kansas and went to Atlantic City. There, he won on the very first horse he rode.

The horse's owner told Charlie, "I'll bet $200 across the board on this horse for you." So when Charlie won, he immediately had a pocket full of money. For a short while he basked in the glow of his newfound independence, but soon found that getting mounts without a contract would not be easy.

While in Atlantic City, he looked up one day and saw his buddy Lil Epp from Ponca City walking toward him in the paddock. Clayton Epperson had signed a contract the year before with Pete Maxwell and gone to Fairmont Park, just like Charlie did in 1950. But after breaking his maiden, Clayton got injured and had returned home to ride out the rest of that year in the bushes.

"I'm lookin' for work. You know any of these old boys around here?" Clayton grinned and stuck out his hand.

"Come on, Buddy," Charlie said. "I think Hirsch Jacobs will start you out galloping. Pretty soon, we'll be riding against each other, just like the old days."

But destiny would take the two bush track boys down separate paths.

Charlie signed a new contract with an agent and soon realized that being under contract to an agent also had its limitations. Charlie's independent nature, his temper, and his immaturity kept him in continual conflict with those in position to control him.

Then came a scandal involving a girl, jail time, and a short, loveless marriage. It took 50 years and DNA testing for Charlie to prove he was not the father of a child. Within two years, the little boy from the bushes who quickly rose to Leading Rider of the Nation had received a harsh introduction to the reality of greed, power, and the price of fame.

But in spite of the personal setbacks and the difficult journey of the agent/owner relationships, it was the love of the ride that kept Charlie Burr in the saddle. And in 1953, Charlie bounced back into the limelight when he rode six horses and won on all of them at Gulfstream Park.

Charlie first met Mildred Lillian Schull at the racetrack in Atlantic City. He was immediately comfortable around Mildred. Strong-minded and outspoken, Mildred had a genuine fiber of honesty that Charlie had not seen in many other girls. He liked what he saw and pursued the young "Yankee" girl. Charlie and Mildred were married on October 6, 1954.

From 1954 to the late '70s, Charlie's career continued to make headlines in newspapers from his hometown to Massachusetts and Florida.

In the Arkansas City, Kansas, paper dated Thursday, February 11, 1954: "Arkansas Cityan Among Tops—Charley Burr of Arkansas City is among five famous jockeys who have ridden more than 1,000 winners."

A grinning Charlie was pictured with Johnny Adams, Steve Brooks, Ted Atkinson, and Jimmy Stout.

From the *Chicago American*, Thursday, May 19, 1955: "Balmoral Meet Lures Burr Back From East".

The article tells about Charlie getting his big start in Chicago five years before, a start that led him to be Leading Rider in 1951: "In almost five years, Charlie has ridden approximately 1,000 winners at major tracks, many of them big races, and has been trusted with such mounts as Dark Star and Count Turf, both of whom went on to win the Kentucky Derby. He has also ridden such class performers as Sub Fleet and Sunglow."

In the same article, 21-year-old Charlie tells the reporter he had done most of his riding the previous two years in Florida and New Jersey: "I saw where they were

On a few occasions, Charlie would ride a horse for a friend on his visits back to Oklahoma. He rode Moonlight Gail to victory for Paul Epperson at Midway Downs in Stroud. Paul is holding Moonlight Gail with Clayton standing behind with his hand on the horse.

Charlie as a professional at age 16 in Florida's Tropical Park.

going to have that coordinated stake and purse plan at Balmoral, Arlington Park and Washington Park. I figured it added up to a lot of money and a lot of good racing, so I made the switch."

Charlie's bush track experience not only kept him on the front-page for more than two decades, it served him well when things went wrong during a race. The farm boy who had gained his early experience by buying and breaking green colts on Grandma's farm, then riding half-broke horses on the bush circuit, knew how to stick to the saddle like an Oklahoma sandbur.

One day at Rockingham Park in the fifth race, Charlie was riding Fleet Musketeer when his saddle started slipping. The pommel pad flapped behind him as he started down the backstretch and the saddle began to slip toward the horse's belly. Charlie lost his left iron, but managed to keep Fleet Musketeer in a straight line and finished third. As he went under the wire, Charlie was sitting down on Fleet Musketeer and the saddle was on the horse's belly.

The crowd loved the display of horsemanship, and steward Pat Farrell, recognizing the feat, went to Charlie after the race and complimented him on the ride.

Charlie rode against some of the legends. Certain races would stand out in his memory for a lifetime. In Tropical Park in Miami, Florida, riding Sky Wonder, Charlie won over Bill Hartack on Coeur de Fer.

Once, at Churchill Downs in a prep race for the Kentucky Derby, Charlie was running in the fog. He thought he was in front until he saw the rump of a horse four lengths in front. When the horse in front sensed he had company, he caught a gear and disappeared into the fog. Charlie later discovered that the horse in the fog was the famous Swaps he had heard so much about. The rider that day was Willie Shoemaker.

One day in 1956, Charlie was asked by Calumet Farms at Gulf Stream Park to ride the great filly Princess Tierra in a prep race for the Kentucky Derby. They knew that this filly had a world of speed, but was green. Charlie was told to show her around the race track and give her some experience. General Duke, her stable mate, was the favorite in the race and expected to win the Kentucky Derby.

When the gate lifted, the filly went right to the front. Charlie had a nice hold on her as they went into the first turn. She set just off of the rail as they went around the turn. Charlie kept a hold on her and she ran nice and easy. When they came out on the backstretch, she was still in front, running easily. Charlie took her a little to the right and then brought her back in line about three feet off of the rail.

Charlie realized he still did not have any company. When the filly came into the far turn, he asked her to change leads with his movement and the reins. He took a quick look back and realized he was about six lengths in front. Charlie still had a good hold on the reins, and yet the filly had put the field away.

About mid-stretch, Charlie heard Steve Brooks, the first call rider for Calumet Farms, saying, "I'm coming, Charles." Then Brooks, on General Duke, got up just in time to beat the filly by a head, with Charlie still keeping her in hand.

Calumet Farms trainer Jimmy Jones came out to pick up the filly and started raising hell with Charlie for the way he rode Princess Tierra. Then fellow trainer Ben Jones came out and told Jimmy to shut up and apologize to Charlie, and to thank him for saving the filly's maiden.

In the 1960s, Maryland owner and trainer Billy Turner asked Charlie to ride a colt named Pantany. It was the colt's first race. When Charlie got to the gate with him, six men were there, one of them with a bullwhip, to get him loaded. They beat him to get him in, and he was last in the gate. When the gates opened, Charlie was last out and got beat by 55 lengths. The horse did not run a step.

Charlie could tell that the colt did not like to be touched, and told Turner, "Let me ride him back and make some changes."

Turner agreed, and entered him later in a $5,000 maiden. Charlie told Turner, "I don't want any lead pony with him. I'll take him out of the paddock myself and I don't want any whips at the gate."

When the gate lifted in the next race, Pantany broke on top and won by eight lengths. He paid $148 for a two-dollar ticket.

Turner asked Charlie to ride Pantany in his third race, but Charlie already had agreed to ride a filly, Lovely Lane, for a Maryland trainer. Ironically, it was another young bush track rider named Eldon Nelson who agreed to ride Pantany.

Charlie had talked briefly with Eldon before. They discovered they were both veterans of the bushes near Ponca City, Eldon leaving for Kansas City about the time Charlie started riding the bush track circuit. Because Eldon owned a farm in Cedar Vale, Kansas, and Charlie had bought property near Arkansas City, the two lived only 40 miles apart.

Charlie told Eldon his secrets about riding Pantany, and Eldon beat Charlie in the race by a head. Later in the jock's room, Charlie told Eldon he might not give him quite so much information next time.

The two boys' paths crossed many times over the years. On June 8, 1957, Charlie won a stakes race on Better B. Fifteen years later, in 1972, Eldon won the Preakness on BBB, a son of Better B.

In 1957, Charlie became a father. Cyrise Ann was born in November of that year. With a wife and daughter, Charlie found it increasingly difficult to live the life of a jockey, following the racing circuits. Two years later, on July 4, 1959, Mildred gave birth to a boy, Charles Edwin Burr, Jr.

In 1960, Charlie and his family had a modest home in North Miami Beach where they spent the winter months, and a summer home in Mt. Holly, New Jersey, where Charlie could commute to Monmouth Park. In a feature article about Charlie in the *Monmouth Park Bugle*, dated Saturday, July 2, 1960, appeared the following: "At Monmouth Park, he is handling the bulk of the riding for trainer Bill Mitchell and the Meadowbrook Stable. His engagements are handled by "Slim" Edwards, who is credited with being one of the best jockey agents in the business."

At several points in his life, Charlie gave up riding for brief stretches of time, bought property in Arkansas City, Oklahoma and Maryland, and tried to make a living raising and training horses. But the need for money always lured him back to the track.

In 1962, more than a decade after Charlie Burr left the Oklahoma bush tracks, he rode what he later considered "his best mount." Charlie piloted Mongo, owned by Mrs. Richard C. Dupont, to win 11 stake races and two graded stake races—the Trenton

Charlie Burr won The United Nations Handicap on Mongo in Atlantic City in 1962.

Handicap and the United Nations Handicap.

Mongo was a 3-year-old running against older horses in the United Nations, so that made the victory even sweeter. Charlie rode him in one race where the odds were 25-1, and Mongo won by 25 lengths.

In the Sunday morning *Philadelphia Inquirer*, dated November 4, 1962, an article by Bill Hall read:

Mongo Upsets Carry Back in Trenton Handicap

Montpelier's Mongo, meanwhile, who copped the $46,420 first money, ran the same race he used to take the United Nations, and Burr declared: "He's as game as they make 'em. . . . I think Carry Back had a head, or maybe a neck on us passing the 70-yard pole, but I asked Mongo one more time, and he came up strong."

A picture of that race shows Mongo and Carry Back neck and neck. The caption reads: "Mongo, ridden by Charlie Burr, outlasts Cary Back on sloppy track, made heavy

Charlie Burr won The Arkansas Derby on Prince Davelle in Oaklawn in 1964.

by all-day rain, to win the $75,000-added Trenton Handicap at Garden State Saturday by a nose."

Another great race for Charlie—that ended in a missed opportunity—was winning the Arkansas Derby on Prince Davalle in an upset victory in 1964. At Oakland Park, before a crowd of 18,608 people, Charlie won on Prince Devalle by an amazing six lengths. The horse, however, later turned up with an injury and was unable to run in the Kentucky Derby.

In *The Sentinel-Record*, dated Sunday, April 5, 1964, the front-page headline read: "Prince Davelle Racks up Easy Arkansas Derby Win." The accompanying picture showed Charlie and Prince Davelle with a commanding lead.

Charlie hung up his tack for a while after that race. He bought a horse ranch in Oklahoma and decided to devote more time to his wife and two young children. It was difficult to drag his family with him on the race circuit and even more difficult for Charlie to leave them behind. But very soon, he hired a manager for the ranch and

Charlie Burr won the Pacifica Handicap riding Greco Time owned by Mrs. W.J. Hock. In the win picture holding the horse is James W. Smith, trainer and the son of Tom Smith who trained Seabiscuit.

returned to the track. Charlie wanted to both ranch and ride, but later admitted, "you have to be on the scene to make anything go."

Back on the track a year later at Suffolk Downs, Charlie won in the opening race, riding Shell Stable's Star Tar to victory. The Burr was back in the saddle.

From 1959 through 1964, Charlie won five graded stake races. They were: 1959, Black Helen Handicap on Rosewood; 1960, Delaware Oaks on Rash Statement; 1961, Vineland Handicap on Frimanaha; 1962, Trenton Handicap on Mongo; 1964, Arkansas Derby on Princess Davelle.

On a few occasions, Charlie would ride a horse for a friend on his return visits to Oklahoma. A win picture in 1964 shows Charlie up on Moonlight Gail, owned by Paul Epperson, Clayton's father.

In 1967, at Tanforan, California, Charlie won the Pacifica Handicap. In the win picture is trainer James W. Smith, son of Tom Smith who trained Seabiscuit, and owner of the horse, Dorothy Hock, who then owned the Green Bay Packers.

In 1970, Charlie had a trainer's license at Delaware Park, and two horses in Mildred's name. He was quoted as saying, "With only two horses, I don't need any stable help. I'm my own groom, hot walker and exercise boy."

At 36, Charlie still weighed only 112 pounds, but anyone who knew him knew that the little man had a big heart. As age began to subdue the "terror" in Charlie, he went out of his way to help younger riders get a start.

Charlie took a special interest in Cheryl White, a black jockette from Orwell, Ohio, who became known as the first black female jockey in the United States. He could see that the teenager had talent, and paved the way for her to get started by allowing her to live with his family so she could attend the Laurel race meet.

An article in *The Baltimore Sun*, dated Friday, October 1, 1971, stated: "But Charles Burr, national riding champion in 1951 with 310 winners, believed Cheryl deserved a chance at the beginning and has taken her career to heart—and brought it to Maryland."

A family tragedy greatly impacted Charlie in 1972, when his 13-year-old son died of brain cancer. Reeling with grief and faced now with mid-life decisions, Charlie struggled to find his way back. In the end, the same fighting spirit that had driven him his entire life helped him regain balance and press on.

In an article appearing in 1973, 39-year-old Charlie was pictured with Jim Powell, leading jockey at Turf Paradise in Phoenix, Arizona. The two-column article told about Charlie's impressive accomplishments and commented that Burr was among the many new faces cropping up in the jockey colony that year.

A special race was run in honor of Charlie on August 6, 1986 at Suffolk Downs in Massachusetts.

In the summer of 1976, Charlie applied to the New Mexico Racing Commission for a steward position at La Mesa Park in Albuquerque, and was accepted. Soon, however, he returned east.

In the December 1978 *Racing Journal* was written: "Charles Burr, who was the nation's leading rider in 1951 and who is considered one of the premier jockeys of all time, has returned to the saddle.

Burr, who is now 44 and a picture of health, rode recently at Penn National, but plans to make his base of operations in Maryland, where he has ridden previously with great success. . . ."

Although a Triple Crown race win eluded Charlie, in his career he competed twice in the Preakness Stakes, finishing fourth in 1953 on Ram 'O War and fifth in 1963 on Sky Wonder.

On August 19, 1980, life as Charlie had known it came to an end. As a favor for a trainer, Charlie crawled on a horse named Lloyd Lloyd at Bowie Race Track in Maryland. The trainer had asked him to blow the horse. It had rained that morning, and water stood in puddles on the track. Lights were glaring from the grandstand, reflecting off of the pools of water, and spooked the horse, who threw Charlie, then turned and pawed him on the back.

The horse broke Charlie's neck, and while he survived, his riding days were over. With one strike of a hoof, Charlie became a quadriplegic. He spent the next five months in the hospital.

Charlie had no insurance. He always had been a tax-paying citizen of Kansas, however, so the state sent a Lear Jet to pick him up and return him to Arkansas City, where he and Mildred resided for the next 28 years.

During the writing of this book, after 28 years of what many people would consider, "no quality of life," Charlie still greeted every visitor with a big smile and sparkling eyes. His bed sheets were decorated with boots and saddles, he had pictures of horses on every wall, and he watched the races daily from his bed. His tragedy did not dampen his lifelong passion for racing.

Mildred took care of her husband around the clock with little help, refusing to take too much praise for her loyalty.

"He took care of me for 25 years," she said. "After the accident, it was my turn."

Charlie often was approached by eager young reporters, usually just before the running of the Kentucky Derby, the Preakness or the Belmont. One question always asked was, "What was it like back then, in the bushes?" Charlie, with good-natured humor, would tell them enough to satisfy their curiosity without revealing much detail.

Willie Shoemaker donated to Charlie a wheelchair in 2000. He talked to Charlie often. Ron Turcott, who rode the great Secretariat to fame in the Belmont in 1973, taking the Triple Crown of racing, sent Charlie a birthday card in 2008, on Charlie's 74th birthday. One special boyhood friend, George Jordan, demonstrated his love and loyalty by showing up every Friday to sit and watch the horse races on TV with Charlie.

From time to time, other riders and friends from the past would pick up the phone and call Charlie, but the fellow riders who remained ever loyal to Charlie and visited him often, perhaps the only two men who could fully appreciate the fact that Charles Burr rode his last race with dignity and great courage, were fellow bush track boys Clayton Epperson and Eldon Nelson.

Panama, R.P., Sunday, March 23, 1952

RIDING HIGH - - - - By Alan Maver

Charlie sparing with Sugar Ray Robinson

CHARLIE BURR, WHO BECAME THE 7th JOCKEY EVER TO WIN 300 OR MORE RACES IN A SEASON WAS GALLOPING OFF WITH 1951 RIDING HONORS

Jockey C. Burr Rides Six Consecutive Winners — March 30, 1953
Out of Six Mounts — Gulfstream Park

Charlie's 6 consecutive wins in 1953 at Gulf Stream Park

An injury in 1980 at Bowie racetrack left CHARLIE BURR a quadriplegic. His wife of 50 years cares for Charlie 24/7. He is one of the unsung heroes of the racing world. At just 16 years old, Charlie accomplished numerous records, but the true quality of the man was always his generosity and kindness to others. Thanks to his wife Mildred, Charlie is hanging in there, wishing he could get back up one more time.

Charles Burr "1976"

Years after his accident, Charlie was recognized in the July 2007, Edition 49, of the official newsletter of the Don MacBeth Memorial Jockey Fund.

CHAPTER 3

Glen Eldon Nelson

The Buck Sheep

Eldon awoke to the trill of a song sparrow singing his heart out from the old cottonwood tree near the farmhouse. Moving slightly to get away from the sharp pain of a toenail poking him in the back, he snuggled deeper into the warm quilts.

The enthusiastic bird may have been announcing spring in Tonkawa, Oklahoma, but the March wind howling across the screened-in porch where he and his two sisters slept still held the bite of winter.

Eldon's mother, Adelene, cracked the back door and stuck her head out.

"Rise and shine," she called. "Breakfast is ready."

Eldon's two older sisters, Maxine and Evelyn, began to stretch out in the double bed. Because they slept on the opposite end of the bed from Eldon, any time they moved he had to dodge bayonets of sharp toenails.

Eldon hopped quickly out of bed, slid into his overalls, and went into the warm house, where the smell of browning ham on top of the wood stove caused his mouth to water. His father, Glen, sat at the table with a cup of coffee and watched as Eldon climbed into his chair and up onto his special stool. Glen Nelson had made the wooden stool to set in the chair to elevate his 6-year-old son up to the table.

"After breakfast, you take care of your pigs and gather the eggs," Glen said to Eldon. "Later this morning, you can help your sisters in the garden."

Glen hesitated, waiting for a reply.

"Yes, sir," Eldon said, taking the cool cup of milk his mother offered.

As soon as Eldon's sisters shuffled in and helped put the food on the table, Adelene motioned for them to sit as she slid her toddler, Jeanie, into the high chair. Glen bowed his head and gave the blessing.

Breakfast at the Nelson household held little time for idle conversation. Glen lined out his children with their daily chores, devoured his ham and eggs, then excused himself. He took his cap and jacket from the peg by the door.

"I'll be in the east pasture with the team all morning," he said, turning back to Adelene, who by then had little Jeanie on her hip.

"We'll bring you some iced tea and dinner," she said.

Eldon finished eating, climbed down from the table and followed Glen out the door. In January, Eldon had turned 6 years old. He felt sure that he would start to grow very soon. He wanted in the worst way to be able to help his dad more.

Glen never had shown disappointment in the fact that his only son, Glen Eldon Nelson, was extremely small. He never expressed any alarm that after fathering two normal daughters, he had a son who would, by most standards, be considered a runt. But once, when Glen had no idea Eldon was listening, his dad confided in Adelene "I'm not sure that boy is going to grow."

Although Glen probably did worry about his son's size, he never gave Eldon special treatment when it came to work. The boy had full responsibility for the pigs and chickens, along with endless barn and gardening chores that he shared with his sisters. Although Eldon could not carry as much in a slop bucket as could his big sisters, or a full bucket of water or milk, he learned to make several trips back and forth without complaint.

Everyone in Glen's family worked hard. In 1933, any family trying to scratch out a living on an Oklahoma farm knew that working hard meant at least the possibility of eating regularly. Eldon worked extra hard to do his share. He might be the smallest of the family, but he never would be called lazy.

And although Eldon's size proved to be a disadvantage in his youth, being small greatly contributed to his destiny. As an infant and toddler, Glen always tossed Eldon up on one of the plow horses, Colonel or Dan, to make sure he did not get stepped on. Anytime Glen was working around the barnyard or in the field, or was talking to a neighbor, little Eldon was horseback. So, it was that from his earliest memory, Eldon had been at home on a horse.

All in all, Eldon's big sisters treated him well, and his baby sister, Jeanie, was sweet, but the worst thing about his older sisters was their passion for playing house and their delight in using him for their baby doll. Eldon put up with the nonsense for a long time, accepting any number of bribes for allowing his sisters to dress him up and jerk him around by the hand while they played out their silly games. But when Eldon started first grade, he took a stand.

By age 7, because of the treatment he received at the hands of his cousins and the neighbor boys, Eldon knew that life as a runt was not going to be easy. When it was time for him to start school, Glen told the girls, "Don't fight his fights for him. He'll learn when to fight and when to run. I don't want you girls making a sissy out of him."

Hearing that made Eldon realize that life out in the world was going to be a little tougher than it had been around the farm with big sisters to protect him. But it also made him feel like a man. He told his sisters right then, "There will be no more baby doll pretend games."

Evelyn quickly became Eldon's favorite sister, because unlike the other girls who constantly played house and talked of boys, Evelyn loved being outside and shared Eldon's passion for horses. It was Evelyn who lifted him from the fence to the back of one of the plow horses when he asked. And it was Evelyn who rode bales of hay with Eldon in the barn on cold winter afternoons, while the Oklahoma wind banged against the loft door. Together, Evelyn and Eldon became Old West outlaws, constantly seeking adventure from the back of a pretend horse.

But Eldon's venture into the real world had been harsher than he expected. Because of his size, he was an immediate target for bullies. Fighting and running became an everyday occurrence the first few weeks of school. It was common for Eldon to have a black eye, a scrape, or a torn shirt. And although the constant bullying never really ceased, Glen had been right. Eldon soon learned who he could whip and who he had to outrun.

In the third grade, Eldon realized that school would forever be a battleground. When he entered third grade, the first-graders were bigger than he was. But little Eldon slowly evolved into a small package of dynamite. Work on the farm had made him strong for his size, and fighting gave him speed. He learned how to pick up an "equalizer" when older boys got after him. He learned how to look an adversary in the eye and challenge an empty threat. By age 8, Eldon already had learned to master his fears.

Eldon was 8 years old in 1935, a time when life for most farmers in Oklahoma was difficult and about to get tougher. The drought, which had begun four years earlier, began to peak and brought the dust bowl on the heels of the Great Depression. Hundreds of farmers lost their land to foreclosure, and rural populations declined as families moved to town to find work and survive.

The physical and emotional load broke strong men and women during that era, but Eldon's mother remained a stabilizing factor through the worst of times. She had a sense of humor that shined even on the darkest days.

Adelene's sister, Eldon's Aunt Jane, lived nearby and often visited. It was common to hear the two women howling with laughter from the kitchen. Adelene had a talent for taking a miserable situation and putting a humorous spin on it. Whether she was cooking and canning pork at hog-killing time, hanging up endless baskets of wet clothes on the line, or weeding the long rows of beans in the garden, Adelene Nelson always had the ability to make her family grin.

Sometimes, while working in the garden in the smothering Oklahoma humidity, swatting mosquitoes, itching, and sweating, Eldon would wait silently for one of his mother's quips. With one funny sentence about their situation, Eldon's mother would have them laughing, sitting on the ground, and adding individual ingredients into a wonderful stew of togetherness.

Adelene's brand of special humor, her ability to always choose happiness over suffering, served Eldon well on his journey through adolescence.

Glen Nelson, with the responsibility of five kids and another on the way, took life a little more seriously. Although fair, he put up with little nonsense. He used a razor strap to keep his crew in line, telling them simply, "There are too many of you to argue with, so you do what I say."

But Glen sometimes could create sparkling moments of laughter for the entire family. Once, Adelene ordered a new pair of shoes from the Sears and Roebuck catalog. Adelene was not one to be frivolous. She always put her children's and husband's needs first, but her old shoes were falling apart and, at Glen's insistence, she ordered new ones for her birthday.

The day the shoes arrived in the mailbox, Adelene made a celebration out of it. She made lemonade, seated everyone out on the screened-in porch that evening, put the shoebox on her lap, and slowly opened it. With eyes wide and a big grin, she carefully took the durable, lace-up shoes out of the box and held them up for everyone to see.

Exclamations of awe brought giggles from Adelene as she bent and tried to slide her foot into the shoe. Her face fell, however, when her feet would not squeeze into the shoes.

"They sent the wrong size," Adelene said, her voice unusually small and distraught. It had taken weeks for the shoes to arrive. Now they would have to be sent back and it would take months for her to get her new shoes.

Eldon watched his mother's eyes fill with tears and he struggled to think of something to say that might help. Glen jumped from his chair and grabbed the shoes.

"They just need stretching," he said.

Sitting back in his chair, Eldon's dad untied his dusty brogan boots and, to everyone's dismay, tried to cram his big feet in Adelene's shoes. Of course he could not get his feet completely in the shoes, but did manage to stick his big toes far enough in that he could scuff around the porch. Adelene was first to laugh. Her cackle of glee brought laughter from the girls, and Eldon joined in with relief that his mother's sadness had disappeared. The shoes were returned, and months after her birthday Adelene finally received her belated present in the correct size.

The picture of his stern father coming to his mother's rescue by "stretching" her birthday shoes remained with Eldon forever.

In mid-April of 1935, 8-year-old Eldon was working in the garden one afternoon with his sisters. The three of them joked and visited as they bent over the rows of peas, green beans, and onions. Eldon's job that morning was to pull the green onions, tie them in bunches, and hang them in the barn. The girls were to pick and shell the first batch of snap peas. The kids would then kill two pullets, clean them, and get them ready to fry.

It had been a lean winter. The pork had disappeared in January. Eldon remembered his mother making a ritual out of opening that last mason jar of cooked pork. Adelene made a wonderful pan of gravy from the grease drippings in the jar, and told everyone, "This is kind of like the Last Supper, kids. Enjoy it."

Since that cold night, the family had survived mostly on cornbread, oatmeal, milk gravy, and bread. In the early spring, they had mountains of turnips and sometimes poke greens, but no meat.

The young chickens were finally old enough to butcher. By irrigating from the well, Glen had managed to make the family garden thrive. Long, straight rows of corn, onions, and beans covered half of an acre, along with blossoming tomato and potato plants. As Eldon carefully pulled the plump green onions and tied them in bunches, his mouth watered. He could already taste the fried chicken, mashed potatoes, and his mother's gravy over a thick slab of her homemade bread. The feast would be served on Sunday, after church.

The girls suddenly stopped their chatter, and they and Eldon stood, listening. Glen came galloping up from the pasture on Dan, leading Colonel, and Eldon knew immediately that something was very wrong. He never had seen his father run the horses.

"Get to the house, now," Glen screamed.

Before Eldon and the girls reached the porch, a black cloud of dust engulfed them. Eldon turned to see his dad coming through the cloud, but he could not see the barn. The girls coughed and choked as they went to work helping Adelene wet sheets and towels in the sink. Eldon helped stuff the towels under the outside doors while his sisters helped hang wet sheets over the windows, but in spite of their efforts the dust seeped through every crack. By the time the storm passed, Eldon could write his name on the furniture, the floor, and the walls.

The family followed Glen outside and looked at the devastation. The garden had disappeared. The combination of heavy wind and whirling dust had taken the tender plants off even with the ground. The field of wheat that recently had grown just over Eldon's knees lay obliterated, half-buried in uneven mounds of dirt. In the orchard, peach and apple blossoms lay scattered everywhere on the ground. Leaves on the trees hung so heavy with dust that green limbs creaked from the weight.

Young chickens lay dead in the barnyard, smothered by the suffocating dust. The pigs coughed and wheezed from their wallow, which the wind had dried up. The milk cows bawled from the barnyard with eerie, muffled voices, disguised by dust.

In less than an hour, the family's entire food supply for the year was destroyed.

Glen cleared his throat and tried to spit, but the effort produced only a tiny hard wad of mud that shot out of his mouth like a bullet. Even Adelene could not muster enough courage at that moment to think of something to lighten the darkness.

Two weeks later, Eldon overheard a conversation between his mother and father. "It's not charity, Glen," Adelene said. "It's necessity. All of the neighbors are getting the food assistance. It's just until we can replant and get back on our feet. What else are we going to do?"

The next day, Eldon rode with his father into town. He watched his proud father hesitate in the pickup, take a deep breath, and then walk on into the building. He noticed how Glen ducked his head, cap in hand, when it came time to sign for the block of cheese, the canned peaches, and beans.

As his dad reached to get the food, one of the ladies doing the paperwork in the office said, "These dumb farmers, having more kids than they can feed."

Eldon watched his father's face flush.

"Lady, you can say any damn thing you want about me, but if you say one more word about my kids. . . ."

Glen stood for a moment in the strained silence, picked up the box of groceries, and left.

Sometime in Eldon's ninth year Glen purchased a ram; the buck sheep and Eldon quickly formed an interesting relationship. Because Eldon's chores were centered mostly in the barnyard and the ram usually was penned in the barn lot, the two saw each other on a daily basis.

Eldon quickly learned that buck sheep are not the friendliest of creatures. Any time Eldon would turn his head or back to the ram, he would charge and butt him. The old ram's head was broad and powerful, and he had thick horns, so the assault was not gentle.

Eldon tried all manner of things to befriend the ram, but eventually found out his options were to pick up an equalizer and hit him or not turn his back, because the stupid buck sheep had no interest at all in friendship.

Glen borrowed a Jersey bull to breed his milk cows one week, and Eldon watched in disbelief when the old ram lowered his head and ran straight for the bull. Before the bull could recover from the first attack, the ram cut a quick circle and came in for a second swat. Eldon was amazed when the bull moved to the far corner of the barn lot in complete submission.

The uneasy relationship between Eldon and the buck sheep became a kind of game after a while. One morning when the ram charged at Eldon, he dodged to one side and then playfully jumped on the sheep's back. To his surprise, he could lift his feet and actually ride the critter. The angry buck sheep took off with a burst of speed and ditched Eldon quickly, but Eldon came up laughing. He had longed to have something to ride. Although the buck sheep was not as good as his own pony, maybe he would do temporarily.

So it began. In his spare time, Eldon would walk across the barnyard, baiting the ram into charging. Eldon would dodge the lowered head by jumping to one side, then quickly grab and twist both of his hands into the ram's wool and jump aboard. The ram would bolt across the barnyard corral, kicking and bucking. The ram's loose hide slipped from side to side, greatly hindering Eldon's attempts to stay astride, but slowly he learned to use his knees and lean forward, giving him better balance.

After just a few days, Eldon enjoyed longer and longer periods of riding before the sheep sent him either sprawling over its head into the fence, or trampled him underfoot in a fresh pile of soft manure.

One day, several weeks after the ram riding began, Eldon was helping Glen fix a leak in the water trough, smearing hot tar on the outside of the tank. The ram snuck up behind Eldon and butted him hard, flattening him on the ground. Glen reached over, picked up a plank with a metal bolt in it, and hit the ram right between the eyes. The ram fell to the ground, kicked, and then lay still.

Eldon had mixed feelings about the apparent demise of his "horse." The ram really had few redeeming qualities, and yet Eldon had grown close to him. He had not told his father about riding the ram, because he was sure his dad would forbid it.

Eldon watched the ram closely for any sign of life. Glen picked up the bucket of tar and started toward the barn.

"If he dies, come and get me," Glen said matter-of-factly. "We'll butcher him."

For the next few minutes, Eldon stared at the ram. As hungry as he stayed, the idea of eating the ram somehow did not whet his appetite. In the comic books he had read and the Old West stories he remembered, he never had heard of a cowboy eating his horse.

Relief flowed through Eldon when the ram first shook a leg, slowly opened his eyes, and wobbled back on his feet. It took the ram several days to physically recover, and Eldon slipped him extra grain and once even tried to rub him behind the ears, but the ram wanted no part of that. He snorted and ran off.

In the weeks to come, it became apparent that the ram would never be quite the same. He would sometimes lower his head and start toward Eldon, but just before he took that first step he seemed to have a burning recollection from the past that stopped him in his tracks. The ram would snort, turn and retreat to the corner of the corral.

Once or twice Eldon cornered him and managed to jump on his back, but the ram would no longer run or buck, simply lower his head.

Just as Eldon's confidence in riding had started to excel, he had lost his mount. Now even hungrier for a horse to ride, Eldon immediately began to look for a substitute for the ram. He considered the milk cows, but knew his father would skin him with the razor strap if he bothered the cows into not giving milk. He tried a pig or two, but the noisy, squealing pigs immediately brought his sisters running toward the barnyard to see what was happening.

Circumstances smiled on young Eldon later that same summer, when his uncle arrived one day with a Quarter Horse named Trixie. The mare had been used to work cattle and she could turn on a dime. From day one, Eldon spent every spare minute he had riding Trixie.

Because there was no saddle, Eldon and his sisters would find a ditch, then patiently lead the mare down into it so they could jump on her back. Sometimes, three or four of them would ride her at once. Oftentimes Trixie would toss them all off into a giggling heap of tangled arms, legs, and bruised bodies, then run off bucking in victory. But within an hour, the kids would have her cornered, back to the ditch, and be riding off for another adventure.

One bright afternoon, Glen showed up from town with an old Army saddle for Trixie. Eldon stood by with racing heart as he watched his dad place the saddle on Trixie's back and begin to cinch it. What would it be like to actually sit in a real saddle?

Eldon loved Trixie dearly, but the little mare had her faults. She liked to pin her ears and bite at the kids when they would start to get on her back. Sometimes, she would bite at the cows if they annoyed her. That day, she made the mistake of biting Glen when he went to saddle her.

Eldon watched as Trixie struck out at Glen with her teeth, ripping his shirt and bringing blood. Glen's face reddened and he cursed, but he did not try to hit the mare. He handed the reins to Eldon.

"Hold her," he said, and walked away.

When he returned, Glen held a short length of a two-by-four in his right hand. Eldon was horrified. He remembered the episode with the buck sheep and knew what was coming. Would his father kill the horse or forever break her spirit? Glen Nelson's face burned scarlet and held a stubborn expression of resolve. Eldon knew better than to say anything when his father was upset.

He watched as Glen began to snug the cinch with his left hand. When Trixie struck out again, Glen hit her hard on the nose with the two-by-four. The mare screamed in pain and held her nose high, jumping around.

"Now, you stand up there and knock that nonsense off," Glen said.

To Eldon's complete dismay, Trixie never tried to bite anyone again. She would turn her head when he cinched the saddle or started to mount, but she would hesitate, remembering the lesson of the two-by-four.

One Sunday after church, Eldon managed to get away on Trixie without any of his sisters begging to go along. Because it was next to impossible for him to catch and saddle the mare by himself, he seldom got to ride Trixie alone. But that day, when the girls were all settled in for a nap, he climbed up on the corral fence and enticed Trixie over with an apple core. He grabbed her, attached a rope to her halter, and then led her to the ditch where he finally managed to saddle her.

A burning sense of freedom and independence filled him when he kicked the mare into a gallop across the field.

Riding Trixie alone became Eldon's passion. The sense of freedom and power he felt galloping through the woods on the mare helped him forget he was still less than four feet tall. He loved to imagine himself a great cowboy hero, and he played endless pretend games on the mare. Sometimes Trixie would get tired of having the hot saddle on her back and she would buck until she sent Eldon flying. But Eldon would not stay off for long. The more Trixie tried bucking him off, the better he got at staying in the saddle.

Eldon's adventures on Trixie took on a new dimension one day, when some neighbor boys happened by, riding their gelding.

"This gelding is a lot faster than any horse around here. He can't be outrun," the boys bragged.

By then, Eldon had been running Trixie every chance he got when he was away from the watchful eyes of his mother and sisters. The little mare was quick for a short distance, and Eldon was confident in his ability to ride her. He immediately took up the challenge.

"Trixie can outrun him," Eldon said quietly.

The boys began to grin, and after a huddle of private conversation, one said, "We'll bet you a chicken."

Eldon considered the bet. His dad would probably skin him if he lost a chicken gambling on a horse race. But Eldon quickly decided the whipping he might receive would not be any more severe for two chickens.

"Make it two and you have yourself a race," Eldon said.

The next afternoon, the boys appeared at the edge of the Nelson farm at the appointed time. One boy walked along carrying two chickens. Evelyn, appointed to hold Eldon's two pullets, stood at the edge of the woods, waiting for the race to begin. It ended almost before it started, when Trixie got the jump on the gelding and burst forward with ears flat against her head. The little mare outran the gelding by three lengths.

Eldon took his first "purse" of two chickens to his mother. He considered the possibility that his father would still react badly to his gambling, but decided to take the chance. It had been awhile since the family had fried chicken for dinner.

Adelene Nelson looked down at her 10-year-old son, still less than four feet tall, as he told the story of the bet, the horse race, and the win. Her mouth twitched down into a frown.

"You better stop that," she warned. "You could get killed."

But she wiped her wet hands on her apron, accepted the two chickens, and giggled.

The Nelson family had fried chicken for dinner that very evening. Eldon knew that his mother had explained the situation to his father. His parents always confided in each other. When the platter of fried chicken came to his father, Glen hesitated, forked two crispy pieces of white meat onto his plate, cast one quick glance across the table at little Eldon, and grinned.

I Could Do That

When he was 16 years old, Eldon stood 4' 5" tall and weighed 75 pounds. He prayed every day for more growth, but had begun to accept the reality that he would never reach his father's 5' 10" height.

Glen Nelson gave up farming and took up carpentry around 1944, changing professions to feed his family. The Nelsons moved from their Tonkawa farm into nearby Ponca City.

Eldon missed life on the farm. Sometimes he ached to be back on Trixie, riding through the woods and open fields. His uncle took Trixie back to his place east of Ponca City and told Eldon he could ride the mare anytime. But by then, leisure time was not that easy to come by. Eldon had quit school and gone to work at the defense plant in Ponca City, making parts for pup tents. He worked at least eight hours a day, leaving little time for fun.

Eldon Nelson, standing right, with, from left, sisters Evon, Evelyn, Maxine and Jeannie. Seated, Nelson's father Glen M. Nelson, brother Ervin, mother Adelene, and sister Velma in the early 1940s.

Eldon's mother, Adelene, and 300 other women worked in the plant along with Eldon and one other young man. When a woman ran a needle through her finger, it was Eldon and the other boy who came to the rescue. Because the other boy was bigger, he would hold the woman still while Eldon backed the sewing machine up, releasing the woman's finger. Sometimes a needle would break and Eldon would extract it from the woman's finger using pliers; blood squirted everywhere during these operations. It was not a job for the weak-hearted, but a task that soon became routine for the two boys.

During those defense plant days, Eldon and Evelyn sometimes took their two younger sisters Velma and Evone to the picture show in Ponca City. At that time, people who had money went downtown to the Poncan Theater on First and Grand. Those less fortunate went to the Ritz on the west side of the railroad tracks, near Union Street and Grand.

The Nelson family had continued to grow. By the time they moved to Ponca City, Eldon had five sisters—Maxine, Evelyn, Velma, Evone, and Jeanie—and a new baby brother, Ervin. Money always was scarce with so many mouths to feed, the reason Eldon quit school to go to work. That is also why the Nelson kids went to the Ritz Theater instead of the Poncan.

The movie always began with a newsreel that gave the audience a quick overview of what was happening in the world. On that day in 1944, the headlines revolved around the much-anticipated end of World War II. Eldon watched the news with interest. He wanted to go into the service, but figured he would never be accepted because of his size. He would love to go sit in the cockpit of an aircraft, behind a gun, and fire away at the enemy.

But that day, dreams of power and glory, of coming home a hero, were interrupted when the sports news flashed across the screen. The Kentucky Derby, the first race of the Triple Crown, was going to run within a week. While the sportscaster talked of the Preakness and Belmont, and the ponies' odds, Eldon sat spellbound, staring at the professional jockey on the screen. Standing proudly on the scales with his saddle in hand, the complete weight—jockey, saddle, and all—registered 101 pounds.

"I could do that!" Eldon thought in a burst of excitement. He grabbed his sister's arm and exclaimed, "I could do that, if I knew how to get there," he said. "I know I could. I'm small enough and I'm a good rider."

Evelyn agreed with a nod of her head, but did not take her eyes from the screen. Going to the movies was a rare treat. She was not going to miss anything by listening to her younger brother babble about what he could do.

"If I don't grow," Eldon continued, "I could do that. I know I could."

"Shuu," said Eldon's longtime girlfriend, Wilma, staring at him with a frown. Eldon and Wilma had been dating for more than a year, but sometimes Eldon was unsure about their relationship. When it came to horses and riding, Wilma had little interest.

Eldon sunk down in the theater seat and got quiet, but his mind raced with the possibilities. Maybe he could find a way to keep riding. Two of his uncles, Glen's two younger brothers, Ray and Dale, worked out in Osage County on a cattle ranch. The first chance he got, he would go out and ride with them. That first chance came when his uncles invited him to come out and help with the cattle one day.

By this time, Eldon had invested some of his hard-earned money on a used Model A Ford. When he quit school and went to work at the defense plant, he was 15 and his father agreed that he should hold back a third of his salary each week for a car of his own. The day Glen and Eldon rattled into the Nelson driveway with the used Model A, the entire family celebrated. Then, with the help of two-by-four blocks affixed to the gas, clutch, and brake pedals so he could reach them, and his father's patience, Eldon began to drive.

Like any teenage boy, Eldon was excited about owning and driving his own vehicle, but his desire to drive directly was linked to his passion to ride. He wanted to accept the invitation from his uncles to help out on the ranch.

So, within days after Eldon became the proud owner of the Model A, he and his sister Evelyn drove out to Osage County and began to ride on the ranch. Riding the cow ponies helped Eldon learn more about staying in the saddle.

Late one afternoon, Eldon's uncles and several of his cousins took Evelyn and Eldon to the small bush track east of Ponca City. The track had no gates, no grandstand, or judge's booth. It was nothing but a simple straightaway track out through a pasture, with two stakes in the ground indicating the start and finish lines.

Uncle Dale had heard about the track and already had taken his boys out to have a little fun racing their ponies. That morning when they arrived, there was a crowd of horses and men standing around talking and exchanging money. Apparently, the men who worked at Continental Oil Company in Ponca City had started coming out to the small bush track on weekends after arguments at work led to match races.

"My colt can outrun your horse for 200 yards," one man said, as Eldon approached the crowd.

"I'll bet 20 bucks he can't outrun my mare for 300," another man said, stepping up.

Eldon stood back with his sister, uncles, and cousins, and watched, fascinated as the men set up one match race after another. They hung out all morning, watching the horses blast out over the flat pasture, kicking up dust, and watching the men when they yelled in victory or cursed in defeat.

Suddenly, Eldon's Uncle Dale had him by the shoulder.

"Eldon, there's a guy over here that wants you to ride in the next race," he said. "I've been telling him about you."

"Me?" Eldon said, suddenly terrified. He never had ridden in a real race like this, where men were watching and people were betting.

"Come on over. It'll be OK. I'll help you get all ready."

Within a few minutes, Eldon found himself being hoisted up onto a huge gelding and given quick instructions. He listened carefully the whole time—and said a silent prayer he would be able to stop the horse at the end of the race.

Things grew very quiet at the starting line. Two men stood 300 yards away on both sides of the finish line, waiting. The man at the starting line dropped his hat. Eldon leaned forward and the horse jumped. Not being used to a jockey saddle or a horse with real speed, Eldon came up high in the saddle and nearly was ejected. But his body strength and size allowed him to regain balance and ride. The horse won by a nose, but Eldon's greatest fears soon were realized. He could not stop the animal. The horse ran off of the track and all the way across the pasture at breakneck speed, with Eldon pulling on the reins. The big gelding reached a barbed-wire fence several hundred yards away, pivoted, and started back. By the time he arrived at the track, he had slowed and Eldon was able to pull him to a stop.

"Did he get away from you, boy?" the owner grinned as he spoke.

Eldon could not reply. His heart hammered in his throat and his mouth felt full of dust. If not for all of those days chasing cows, he knew he would have met his fate in that barbed-wire fence. The man generously gave Eldon five dollars. That was more money than Eldon made working an eight-hour day.

Before the sun set that afternoon, two other men approached Eldon and asked him to ride for them the next weekend. Eldon agreed under one condition—the owners would allow his sister Evelyn to wait at the other end of the track to help stop the horses.

For the next two years, on any given weekend Eldon and Evelyn would be somewhere at a bush track. Often, Wilma went along, but more and more she found excuses not to go. Eldon felt torn between his girl and his passion to ride. He was very fond of Wilma, but between work and riding, he had less and less time for her.

Eldon paid his sister half of his earnings to be his "pickup man." Evelyn, a talented rider, quickly became good at the job. She learned to dash her pony up to Eldon's mount and grab the reins. She would proudly pony the horse back up the track.

Eldon's reputation on the bush tracks spread, and soon anywhere there was a horse race, the Nelson team would show up and make themselves available. The Ponca Indians had a small rodeo and often held races south of Ponca City, on the White Eagle Reservation. Eldon and Evelyn soon made friends with some of the Ponca Indian kids their age, and a certain Indian girl developed a crush on Eldon. It took him a while to understand why she kept missing the bus in Ponca City and asking him to take her home to the reservation. Good-natured Eldon always would oblige and Evelyn would usually go along. They all would climb in Eldon's old Model A Ford that smoked like a chimney because of the drip gas he used to run it, and rattle down the road to the reservation.

One of the many horses Eldon Nelson helped care for during his apprenticeship at Woolford Farms.

Eldon Nelson, center, with trainers John Nerud and Ross Higdon from Woolford Farms following one of his first wins.

Finally, Eldon asked Evelyn why the Indian girl missed the bus so much.

"Don't you know?" Evelyn asked her brother, grinning.

"I guess not. That's why I asked."

"Sometimes I don't know about you, brother," Evelyn said. "She's missing the bus because she likes having you take her home."

Eldon made it a point after that to not be available right after school. He liked the girl, but not in that way. He did not want to do anything that might upset his Indian friends. Besides, his steady girl, Wilma, would not like it if she heard someone had a crush on him.

In late January of 1945, shortly after Eldon's 18th birthday, Glen came in one evening with a draft notice in his hand.

"What in the hell do they think they're doing?" he asked, slamming the notice down on the table.

Adelene picked up the notice and read it, while Glen continued to rave.

"Why in the world would they draft some guy my age who's trying to support seven kids? That's crazy!" he exclaimed. "Surely there's some way I can get out of it. I'm too old to fight in a war."

Adelene looked at her husband and asked, "Don't you know that you've got a son with the same name who's the right age?"

Glen looked stunned for a minute. He picked up the draft notice and read it more carefully.

"I'll be damned," Glen said.

Eldon climbed on the bus bound for Oklahoma City two days later. His parents were not happy about the draft, but he was ecstatic. He wanted to go into the military. "Make me a helicopter gunner," he told the officer at the induction center. "I'll blast hell out of 'em."

But the straight-faced officer told Eldon, "Son, you passed everything except the height requirement. I'm afraid you aren't going."

Eldon got back on the bus to Ponca City with a heavy heart. There was a bigger reason he hoped to go into the Army. Eldon wanted to leave home in the worst way. His girlfriend, Wilma, had dumped him and married her ex-boyfriend, who recently had returned from the Navy. Although Eldon had felt for some time that Wilma did not support his dream to ride, he never once questioned her loyalty or affection. So, with a broken heart, the thought of staying around Ponca City and seeing Wilma with her new husband added to Eldon's misery.

Two months later, on a Saturday night in March, Evelyn introduced Eldon to a man at the bush track in Ponca City.

"Jack Mackey, this is my brother, Eldon," Evelyn said.

"Have you considered riding as a career?" the man asked Eldon immediately.

"Yes, I've thought about it," Eldon replied.

"Have you ever heard of a man named Herbert Woolf, of Woolford Stables in Kansas City?" Mackey asked.

"No, sir."

"Well, he has quite an operation up there," Mackey said. "He raises, trains, and

In the mornings Eldon Nelson dressed for work in exercise pants and boots. However, in the afternoon he always returned dressed in a suit and tie.

races Thoroughbreds. Would you be interested in going up and trying to ride for him?"

Eldon knew nothing about this stranger, and he could tell Mackey was interested in Evelyn. But the fact that his sister introduced them made Eldon feel that the man was probably making a legitimate offer.

"Yes, sir. I'd be real interested," Eldon said.

Jack Mackey turned out to have connections, and within a week Eldon received a phone call from him.

"Woolford Farms in Kansas City, Kansas, has a place for you if you are interested," Mackey said. "You have to have written permission from your folks. You come on up and work for 30 days. If they like what they see, they'll sign you for a three-year contract and teach you how to ride Thoroughbreds."

It was a dream come true for Eldon. He now knew he would never get much bigger. He wanted to get out of Ponca City. He wanted to ride horses. The opportunity seemed too good to be true.

"Yes, sir," he said, "I'll get the permission."

Homesick and Heartbroken

One day in March of 1945, Eldon arrived on the outskirts of Kansas City, Kansas, at Jack Mackey's place. Jack put him up for the night, saying he would take him to Woolford Farms the next day. The following morning, Eldon woke up early. Jack had consumed quite a bit to drink the night before, and when Eldon did not see him stirring, he went to work cleaning stalls.

When Jack finally did come out of the house, he saddled a horse and told Eldon to gallop him around the track near the barn. Eldon jumped up and proceeded out with the horse, but the horse kept pulling away, wanting to go toward a grassy area. The next thing Eldon knew, the horse ducked and ran straight for a jump. Eldon had never seen a jump and did not know what it was. The horse leaped over the first jump, ran to the next, jumped it, then went over the entire course of jumps with Eldon grabbing mane and hanging on for dear life.

Eldon cursed the horse as he walked him up to the barn..

"He does that every morning, son," Jack said, laughing. "You did a pretty good job of staying on him."

Jack seemed to thoroughly enjoy the practical joke. Eldon boiled, but remained silent. He kept that silence on the way to Woolford Farms, wondering what he had gotten himself into.

In his haste to leave Oklahoma, Eldon had given little thought to how much he would miss his family. Other than one short summer on his uncle's farm helping with harvest, in 18 years he never had been away from home. And he soon found out that running away from the pain of a broken heart did not make the misery disappear.

He had made an agreement though, and for 30 days, no matter what, he would keep his word. So, while he cleaned stalls, chopped weeds, milked cows, groomed horses, and mucked out the chicken house, he put all of his angry energy into his work. He never had worked harder in his life. Anytime he finished a job, one of the bosses handed him a pitchfork, a hoe, or a shovel and lined him right out with another chore.

At times he wanted to scream, "What is this? I thought I made an agreement to ride horses?" But Eldon was quiet by nature, and he had given his word. He worked hard, observed, and soon began to understand. A long line of young men from the Kansas City area, all aspiring to be jockeys, filtered in and out of the Woolford Farms bunkhouse that first week Eldon arrived.

Most of the city boys, soft from a life of ease, did not last two days with a shovel in their hands. Many of them would tough it out for five days, then drop from exhaustion. The 30 days of hard labor was an elimination process for the owner, Herbert Woolf. The boys who could endure the 30-day trial period might hold some promise. The boys who could not work hard and take orders were not worth his investment of time and money.

With that realization in mind, Eldon began trying to outwork everyone around him. It became a challenge to see how much he could do in one day. The exhaustion from the hard work helped with his mental struggle in the evenings.

After the day's work, when the boys sitting around in the bunkhouse began to talk about home, about the girl they left behind, Eldon always felt the knot of pain inch into his throat. He already had learned that talking about problems did not make them go away. And talking about his family or even mentioning Wilma's name right before bedtime only intensified the turmoil for him. So, Eldon would simply tell everyone goodnight, hit his bunk, say a prayer, and his tired body would mercifully send him instantly to sleep.

But there was one surprise for Eldon at Woolford Farms that was truly a treat. The first evening he was there, Eldon followed the other boys into the large mess hall and kitchen building next to the bunkhouse. After a day of hard work, he slumped down at one of the long tables for supper, disillusioned with his new job. But Eldon quickly came to life when the cooks carried out huge platters of wonderful fried pork chops, thick gravy, new potatoes, snap beans, and homemade bread with bowls of fresh butter. Eldon never had seen food like that in his entire life.

And just as he thought he had seen everything, the swinging doors to the kitchen blasted open again, and here came the cooks with rich desserts of cobbler, cakes, and puddings.

Every morning, Eldon was the first one up and in the mess hall for breakfast. The other boys teased him about his appetite. He was the smallest of over a dozen boys working at Woolford, but he could eat the most. Eldon took the ribbing with a good-natured smile, just enjoying the food at every meal. He did not tell any of the boys that he knew what it was like to be hungry, that he had gone to bed many times with an empty stomach after working hard all day, or that he had watched his father worry for years about where food would come from to feed the family.

It soon became obvious to Eldon that there was also a catch to all of that rich, plentiful food. They weighed the boys at the end of every week, carefully checking how much they had gained. The boys who started packing on the pounds early were not going to be good jockey candidates. Eldon was lucky. He stuffed himself at every meal, worked hard, and did not gain a pound that first month at Woolford Farms.

Eldon's good fortune to eat and not gain was not shared by many of the other boys. He soon learned that the first challenge of any prospective jockey was weight gain. Most of the young men did gain weight, so they had to limit how much they ate.

Eldon loved the mess hall and kitchen. Not only did it offer a glorious array of colorful, tasty food at all times, but it gave him a connection to his mother, who he missed dearly. The large building with its gleaming hardwood floors and colorful tables draped with linen tablecloths was a far cry from the cramped kitchen in the old farmhouse back home, and it immediately became the main topic of conversation in his letters home to Adelene. She delighted in Eldon's detailed descriptions of the luxurious facility, smelling of baked apples, pastries, and smoked ham. She quickly fired back letters filled with questions.

From day one, when there was a break from work or a down time because of weather, everyone knew they would find Eldon in the kitchen, where he took his tablet and pencil, and wrote long letters while sipping a cup of coffee and eating a slice of pie.

Years later, Eldon learned that the mess hall at Woolford Farms held a special place in Kansas history. It did not surprise him to learn that an underground railroad of sorts had been in place even during the time he had sat, eating his meals in that kitchen. He finally understood why the mysterious sense of love he had felt in that mess hall seemed to go beyond him. The building had been a sanctuary, helping countless others in need.

Herbert Woolf had allowed blacks who he felt were innocent of a variety of charges to hide out in a tunnel below that kitchen until he could safely transport them farther north. Some of these men went to work for him either in the kitchen or at the barns, and remained loyal employees for years.

Eldon worked well with the black grooms and teased with the cooks in the kitchen. He never had been around many blacks, but had loved the Indians in Oklahoma and had accepted them when many people were prejudiced. So he treated the blacks as his equal and they immediately liked and respected Eldon in return.

At the end of his 30-day trial period, Woolf called Eldon to his office and offered him a three-year contract.

"Your parents will have to sign with you, since you aren't of age," Woolf said. "You will work around here just like you have been, but soon you can start to gallop a few horses. After that, it'll all be up to you. You will have your opportunity to ride."

That was what Eldon wanted. He immediately sent the contract home for his parents to sign. The work did not scare him. He liked being around the horse operation, watching the grooms, the breeding program, and watching the trainer school the colts at the barn. As homesick as he was, he knew it was time to grow up. He could not stay home forever.

He knew he had made the right decision in leaving Ponca City. His heartache was still fresh, but in time it would fade. He had made it the 30 days, he could make it for three years.

Because Woolford Farms provided Eldon's room, board, and clothes, he sent most of the money he made that next year home to his father. However, Eldon was 18 and the only boy around old enough to have a car, and that circumstance eventually provided an opportunity for Eldon to have a free Saturday night out. Some of the boys wanted to go into town on Saturday nights, and they got the idea to chip in with enough money to buy the gas and pay Eldon's way into a movie in exchange for a ride.

So, most Saturday nights, with three boys in the front and four in the rumble seat, Eldon would rattle out of Woolford Farms in his old Model A. Some of the boys wanted to party, so they would be dropped off at a bar, while Eldon and a few others would head for the movies.

One night, Eldon went into the bar with the other boys to get their friends. The boys who had been drinking bought Eldon a whiskey and Coke, and it tasted so good that Eldon drank it right down and had several more. It was the first experience he ever had with alcohol, and before they got back to the farm, Eldon had to stop his car and lose the whiskey and Coke.

The next morning, when still-queasy Eldon headed for the mess hall, he remembered the one time he had seen his dad drink. Glen and a neighbor had butchered a calf at the neighbor's house. They had a drink to celebrate, then another, and another. Eldon had helped his dad home that afternoon, and watched Glen vomit and squirm in agony the rest of that night.

So, when the beautiful breakfast of ham, eggs, and toast with apple butter did not taste as good as usual, Eldon made up his mind that drinking was not for him. The lesson served him well many times over the years, when his fellow jockeys would choose to celebrate by drinking.

After months of labor, Eldon finally had an opportunity to ride. By then, he had learned how to groom a horse, to sit a horse correctly, and hold the reins. He learned how to ride into the gate, relax, and be ready. He learned how to watch for the crack in that door, and when daylight appeared and be prepared for the horse to leap.

Soon, he was asked to gallop the broodmares in the long row of stalls, and then one of the studs they used to tease the mares. About every third day, Eldon got to exercise the stud around the track at a fast gallop, cool him out, and then bathe him. Eldon loved to ride the stud. Even though the stallion was old and used only as a teaser, he was full of fire and felt powerful beneath Eldon's legs.

Unlike some of the city boys who never had even seen a horse, Eldon did not take any spills. He had ridden enough and been on the bush tracks long enough that he could stick with anything that bucked or acted up. But he still had a lot to learn.

In a 1956 copy of the *Monmouth Park Bugle*, Jim Raftery wrote of Eldon's early training: "The veteran Ovie Scurlock was stable jockey for Woolford Farms at that time and he undertook to teach the young Oklahoman the finer points of handling Thoroughbreds. Ovie recalls how when Eldon was tossed aboard his first Thoroughbred, a now-forgotten mare, the mare took the bit in her teeth and ran off several miles with the diminutive boy clinging desperately to the postage-stamp saddle. The next day, young Nelson was reluctant to attempt the same mount, but Scurlock and trainer Ed Anspach convinced the youth he could handle the mare, and after heeding their advice he climbed aboard and rode her like a seasoned veteran. From that day onward he gained confidence, learned rapidly, and at Tropical Park in 1947 rode his first race on a recognized track."

In Hialeah, Florida on December 26, 1947, Eldon with Woolford Farms jockeys taking the yearlings out to work in pairs. Eldon on the outside in front with his shirt off.

Sometimes, the endless work and homesickness made Eldon feel as though he had signed his life away and would never get the opportunity to pursue his dream. Then, one day in 1947, he was told that he would be going on the racing circuit.

Eldon could barely contain his excitement that first few days at the track. He enthusiastically rode each mount with a big smile. But he soon learned that he was definitely an apprentice.

The trainer at Woolford Farms was giving him every deadhead, every green horse, every horse straight off the farm that he could possibly find. If Eldon had been of a different temperament, he surely would have rebelled. He had spent more than a year doing hard labor just to get to the track. Now that his big day had arrived, Woolford Farms was not giving him a chance to win.

But, as in all endeavors, with patience and perseverance, opportunity arrived. Eldon chewed on his tongue and kept his mouth shut during those first hard days at the track. He had choices. He could still watch and learn as he served his apprenticeship. He could gain knowledge that would serve him well later. The young bush track rider from Oklahoma rode 40 races before he finally won.

It was Eldon's faith that kept him centered during that first discouraging year on the circuit. At an early age he had learned to trust in God. From day one as a professional, each time he got astride a horse he said a prayer.

When many of the other bug boys got discouraged and turned to drinking or drugs, Eldon continued to pray for guidance. His prayers were answered in 1948, at Tropical Park on a horse named Approval. That evening after the win, when Eldon said a prayer of thanks, he grinned. Maybe because of his patience and trust, God had given his "Approval."

It had rained hard that day at Tropical Park. It just so happened that Approval loved the mud. Later, when Eldon looked back over his lifetime of racing, he would recount several experiences where the mud served him well.

Ross Higden from Oklahoma was training horses for Woolford Farms at that time. That day at Tropical Park, when Eldon won his race, Ross went to the jocks' room and took the assigned riders off the other two races, and put Eldon up. Eldon had his break. He immediately got some well-deserved recognition and began to make more money.

After the Florida meet, Eldon went with Woolford Farms to Chicago. The first week there, Eldon broke his wrist in two places. The horse he was riding made an abrupt turn and tossed him off onto the rail.

At the hospital, Woolf told Eldon, "Son, go home until you get out of the cast."

Woolford Farms paid for everything. Eldon got on an airplane to fly him to Ponca City. He had a pocket full of money, stories to tell, and the beginnings of a professional's confidence. Now, going home would be fun.

New Beginnings

Eldon decided to surprise his folks by returning to Ponca City unannounced. When he walked up onto the porch where he always had slept, he found a stranger in his bed. The girl awoke to Eldon's voice.

"Well, since you're in my bed, I guess that makes you mine," Eldon said.

"I don't think so," the young lady shot back.

Eldon immediately liked Betty Coffman. She was a good kid who had come from a rough situation. Her father drowned in the Chikaskia River near Tonkawa when she was 6 years old, leaving her mother with seven children. Betty's mother had a breakdown after the drowning, and the kids temporarily were put in an orphanage. Now 19, Betty had a grateful heart, and Eldon immediately saw that she was the right kind of girl for him.

At 21, Eldon yearned for a family of his own. It had taken him three years to recover from his first infatuation with a girl. This time, he would move slowly and make sure things were right.

Because of his earlier experience with Wilma and meeting a lot of wayward girls around the race track, it was probably Betty's honesty that first attracted Eldon.

Eldon and Betty spent a lot of time together during the next six weeks. When Eldon went to get on the plane to return to Arlington Park in Chicago, he asked Betty to drive him to the airport.

"Why don't you come with me?" Eldon asked when they stopped at the airport parking lot.

"Not without a ring," Betty said sternly.

"Oh, I can get a ring as soon as we get to the race track."

"No, I don't think so. You get the ring first."

Over the next few months, Eldon and Betty wrote to each other regularly.

During his 1948–1949 campaign, Eldon rode 75 winners and took stakes victories on Delegate in the Hawthorn Spring Handicap, and Mel Hash in the Governor's Handicap at North Randal, Ohio. He went on to become top bug boy on the Illinois circuit that year, with his mounts earning more than $200,000.

On St. Valentine's Day 1948, at Hialeah aboard Coaltown, Eldon shattered the track record and equaled the world record. Coaltown finished 10 lengths in front of the field. From the *New York Herald Tribune*, Tuesday, February 15, 1949:

COALTOWN EQUALS WORLD RECORD OF 1:47.6
FOR MILE AND AN EIGHTH

By Joe Palmer, HIALEAH, Florida, Feb. 14—The fastest mile a racehorse has ever run on an oval track came here today as Calumet's unbelievable Coaltown passed the eighth pole in 1:34 1-5 and then blazed to the finish line in 1:47 3-5 to equal the world record Indian Broom set at Tanforan in 1936 under ninety-four pounds for the mile and an eighth. Coaltown had 114 pounds in the saddle. It was Coaltown's own idea, for Eldon Nelson never laid a whip on him.

Young Eldon won a consecutive triple that day, with Coaltown in the middle of it, and in the process gained the position of leading apprentice rider. He went on to be the leading rider at Hialeah that winter, with 22 firsts. By then, Calumet Farms was paying him $1,000 a week for second call. Eldon rode three great horses—Coaltown, Ponder, and Theory—for Calumet Farms.

In the *Miami Daily News*, sports editor Guy Butler wrote: Contrary to the case with many riders, the stable help of Woolford Farms are all rooting for their boy to make good. For instance, George Marchant, who is Nerud's foreman, says, "This kid is a worker and I don't see how he can miss. He's the best kid around a stable I've seen in a long time."

By the fall of 1948, Eldon knew he could make it as a rider. He could be a good provider. He wanted a family. He knew he would soon ask Betty to be his bride. In talking to his boss about his plans, Eldon learned that he had to get permission from Woolford Farms to get married. That, along with the feeling of being totally owned and controlled by someone, led to Eldon's refusal to ever sign another contract in his racing career.

Once the paperwork was complete and the wedding date set, Eldon received a lot of good-natured ribbing from the guys he worked with at Woolford.

"Hell, leave him alone," one of the grooms finally said. "He's going to make a perfect husband. All he does is eat, work, and pray."

Glen Eldon Nelson married Betty Rose Coffman in the fall of 1948 at the Episcopal Church in Ponca City, Oklahoma. The couple left immediately for Florida, where Eldon had commitments to ride. The Woolford Farms' groom predicted correctly. The union between Eldon and Betty lasted for 56 years, until Betty's death.

Moving from race meet to race meet, living in motels, Eldon promised Betty, "You can travel with me wherever I go. We'll always be together."

In Florida, they moved into their first real home, a small bungalow not far from Tropical Park Race Track. Eldon later went into business with the man who rented them their house. Together, they formed the Cowboy Broadcasting Company, and hired an airplane that flew around over the beaches, broadcasting music and advertising for companies.

A few months after the partnership formed, Eldon's partner told him about an airplane that was for sale. The two discussed the possibility of having their own plane and what that could mean for their business. Having always had an itch to learn to fly, Eldon agreed to go in with his partner and buy the plane. He signed up for flying lessons, but did not tell Betty. She was in the early stages of pregnancy and he did not want her to worry. He told his partner and everyone else to not tell Betty he was taking the lessons.

After Eldon passed his solo test, his partner thought it was probably okay to mention the feat to Betty. That afternoon, Eldon said he was taking off in the plane and he looked over and saw his little pregnant wife. Eldon's partner always parked his car out between the second and third hangar, and would wave to Eldon as he took off and came in. Instead of his partner, Betty was there by the car, staring.

Eldon was going too fast to stop, so he went up, turned, and came back to the runway, knowing he was in deep trouble. When he crawled out of the cockpit, Betty was walking toward him crying.

"You're already in the most dangerous profession in the world," she said, wiping tears, "and now you're doing this to me?"

"But, honey," Eldon tried to explain, "we could fly back and forth to the circuit. It would give us more time at home."

"No thanks," she said, bawling.

Betty put her foot down. Eldon gave in. His wife officially grounded him from flying shortly after he got his pilot's license. Eldon already had learned that marriage was all about compromise, and being the wife of a jockey was not easy. He decided he should not make Betty's life any more difficult than it already was.

The Cowboy Broadcasting Company lasted about a year, then Eldon and his partner got their money back out of the business. Eldon had found it difficult to split his responsibilities between the track and another business. To ride successfully, a jockey had to dedicate himself full time.

In 1949, Betty gave birth to a girl, Eldonna Rose. Shortly after his daughter was born, Eldon's contract with Woolford Farms expired.

"We'd love to sign you back up, Eldon," Woolf told him. "You've done a great job and we think you have a promising career ahead."

Eldon sat and listened attentively. With three years to think about being under contract to someone, he knew before he walked into the plush office what he would do.

"I appreciate the offer, sir, and all you've taught me," Eldon said, "but I need to try to make it on my own."

A few months later, after finding his way through a quagmire of agents and owners, and trying to get good mounts, he met Dan McAuliffe. Eldon liked Dan immediately. A former jockey who had learned and ridden under Sunny Jim Fitzsimmons, and who held both Bantam and Featherweight boxing titles, Dan was honest and hard-working.

Eldon Nelson, left, and Dan McAuliffe. McAuliffe was Nelson's first agent following the expiration of his contract with Woolford Farms.

After talking at length about what they both would do and what they both expected, Dan and Eldon sealed their contract with a simple handshake. It was a partnership that would last more than 25 years.

Even though Betty seldom complained, Eldon began to realize how tired his wife was getting of motel rooms. Before the birth of their second child, Eldon was asked to ride a horse that he immediately had a good feeling about. The odds on the horse were 75-1, so he gave Betty a hundred dollars and told her to bet on the horse. Eldon won on the horse by a couple of lengths, and Betty met him later, grinning and holding a paper bag full of money.

"Hang onto that bag," Eldon told her. "Sunday we'll go looking for a trailer house." With the money from the gamble, Eldon purchased a 30-foot trailer home, and Betty was as thrilled as if he had purchased a mansion. She finally had her own space. The trailer house became home for the next year.

In 1949, Eldon's association with Calumet Farms opened up the opportunity for him to ride Ponder in the Kentucky Derby. Days before the Run for the Roses, however, Eldon suffered a spill and broke his foot, losing the Derby mount. Steve Brooks got the assignment and rode Ponder to victory, proving that Eldon could well have been only the third apprentice in history to win the Kentucky Derby.

In the spring of 1950, Eldon did win the Kentucky Derby Trial, aboard Black George. From the *Courier Journal*, Louisville, Wednesday, May 3, 1950:

BLACK GEORGE UPSETS MIDDLEGROUND BY 2;
HILL PRINCE PUTS ON BEST SHOW IN WORK
Black George made it a 'Black Tuesday' for some highly regarded Derby hopefuls yesterday. Running over a sloppy track, and in weather more suited to sea-going animals than landlubbers, Black George won the Derby Trial at Churchill Downs. . . . 'You have a Derby ride now,' [owner W.H.] Veeneman told Nelson as he con gratulated him for his front-running win.

Eldon went on to finish eighth in the Kentucky Derby.

But problems started to pile up against Eldon, eventually leading him into brief retirement from the racing circuit in 1950. He had several spills in Chicago. From the Ponca City News: "Nelson Is Injured In Turf Accident—Eldon Nelson, local jockey, narrowly escaped serious injury recently when the horse he was riding fell and died under him at Arlington Park."

From another newspaper: "Arlington Park, Arlington Heights, Ill.—Two horses fell during the running of the eighth race today. Danseuse, with Logan Batcheller aboard,

In 1950 Eldon Nelson won the Kentucky Derby Trial on BlackGeorge and finished eighth in the Kentucky Derby. Nelson had wished the track for the Derby had been muddy as Black George liked to run in the mud and he believed they could have won.

fell going into the turn, and Sir Galivator, having Eldon Nelson astride, fell over the prone Shady Brook Farm representative."

Eldon was taken to the hospital following one of the spills, having received a minor back injury, but the spills affected Betty more than Eldon. On several occasions she ended up in the hospital. After the birth of Glen Eldon, Jr., Betty developed a heart problem. Eldon was a husband and father with responsibilities. What would happen to his family if he continued to ride?

During this time in his career, Eldon also was becoming frustrated with his weight. Unlike most jockeys who have to constantly reduce and fight weighing too much, Eldon did not weigh enough. A lot of the trainers were passing him up because they did not like for their horses to carry so much "dead" weight.

The daily pressures and responsibilities were not the only factors in Eldon's 1950 decision to sell his racing saddle and buy a cattle ranch in Kansas. In Chicago, the mafia had taken a strong foothold in the horseracing industry. Racing was big money and they intended to get their share of the take by throwing and manipulating races.

Eldon began to get inklings of threats, but at first did not take them seriously. He soon learned that if you did not play ball with the mafia, they put you over the fence. It got so bad that year, Eldon was unsure about which riders he could trust. Two riders would come up on either side of him during a race, squeeze his mount, then pull away so quickly that his horse would go down.

One trainer who Eldon knew could not be bought was killed by the mob. One jockey ended up missing during that time, another supposedly committed suicide, and a third was found buried in a shallow grave near the highway. Before that year was finished, Eldon, Steve Brooks, and Johnny Adams were getting police escorts to and from the track.

It took Eldon a while to comprehend the seriousness of the situation. For a naïve Oklahoma farm boy, at first the rumors of murder made Eldon shrug. He did not believe any of it. But once he actually began to see the power and potential brutality of the mob, he wanted out. He could not make as much money ranching, but he would be safe. He had to think of his family. What would become of them if something happened to him? His moral fiber would never allow him to throw a horserace for the mafia.

In the fall of 1950, Eldon Nelson walked into the Cowboy Supply in Ponca City, Oklahoma, and traded his jock saddle for a used stock saddle. Setting the saddle on the counter, he told Mr. Shultz, the owner of the Western store, "I've bought me a 500-

acre ranch near Cedar Vale, Kansas. I won't be needing this anymore."

Recognizing Eldon's face from articles in the Ponca City News, Shultz asked Eldon, "Did you win any big races on this saddle?"

Eldon paused, running his hands over the saddle, then said, "I won the Hialeah Handicap on it when I was a bug boy. That was the first race my wife ever saw me win." Without any further discussion, Eldon made the trade, picked up the used stock saddle, and walked out of the store.

Another man standing nearby overheard that conversation and went immediately to the jockey saddle. Paul Epperson had a 14-year-old son named Clayton who had been riding the bush track circuit for four years using a saddle pad. "I think I'll buy that saddle for my son," he said.

Eldon and Betty settled into ranch life with enthusiasm. Eldon stocked his farm with purebred Black Angus cattle and bought a fine bull, Prince Sun Beam, from Oklahoma A&M College.

Trainers and jockeys would give Eldon a call from time to time, and Eldon never completely lost touch with what was happening on the race tracks. One day, he opened the *Arkansas City Travele*r and saw an article on another local Kansas boy who appeared to be doing very well.

Charlie Burr lived in Arkansas City, not more than an hour away from Eldon. The article stated that the young Kansan was on his way to becoming Leading Rider of the Nation in 1951, but that the 17-year-old had paid a total of $15,000 in fines for the year.

Eldon smiled when he read about his fellow hot-tempered reins man. He showed the article to Betty.

"He sounds like a character," he said. "I'd like to meet him one of these days."

After two years of retirement, the bottom fell out of the cattle business. Eldon went to work digging post holes from daylight to dark, for $6 a day. Two years on the farm had done wonders for Betty's health, so Eldon began thinking about returning to the track. About that same time, Eldon's Uncle Ivy returned from the service and volunteered to take over management of the farm. Then, Eldon received a call from Jimmy Watts, wanting him to ride for him. Everything fell in place for the Nelson family to return to the race track.

For the next five years, Watts paid Eldon for first call. Eldon exercised horses in the mornings and helped Jimmy at the barn. If Jimmy had a horse in for the day, Eldon rode it. After his commitment to Jimmy, Eldon's agent, Dan McAuliffe, got him other mounts.

In Detroit, in 1953, shortly after Eldon's return to the track, he was called in by the track steward.

"I'm getting a lot of complaints about you, Mr. Nelson," the steward told Eldon.

Eldon had no idea that in the time he was gone, the race track had begun to film everything. He pleaded innocent to the charges of grabbing saddle pads and throat-latches, to holding another horse back with his leg to get an advantage in a race. The steward took Eldon straight to the office and played a film for him.

Eldon sat very quietly, his face scarlet as he watched himself commit almost every possible sin on the big screen. Not only had he been caught, he had lied about his behavior. Eldon cleared his throat.

"I'll serve my suspensions," he said. "I've been out of racing for several years, and I can see that things have ... progressed. I'll change my ways."

The steward tried to keep a serious face while "imposing" the suspension, but it was a feeble attempt that ended in a big grin.

The year Eldon returned to the race track, he went first to Churchill Downs for the 1953 spring meeting, where he got two mounts. He finished third with the first and won on the second. From Kentucky, Eldon and his family traveled to Detroit and then moved to Washington Park in Chicago, where he was leading rider.

At the beginning of the 1954 season, Eldon won the Inaugural Handicap at Hialeah, and then closed out his Arlington Park campaign by winning on Hasty House Farm's Stan in the $156,000 Arlington Handicap.

One of the talents that served Eldon well throughout his career was the ability to observe other jockeys' strengths and weaknesses. Johnny Adams was scheduled to ride Stan that day at Arlington Park, but Eldon knew that Johnny could not hit left-handed or switch his stick, so Eldon approached him.

"Hey, Johnny," said Eldon, "I'm naturally left-handed. Why don't you put in a word for me?"

Johnny did and Eldon ended up riding Stan. The horse stumbled and was in last place, but Eldon picked up his head and went to clucking to him. Stan lugged in and hit the hedge, but Eldon got him back and won the race.

On the front page of the sports section in the Sunday edition of the *Tulsa World* on August 1, 1954, the article on the race read:

HASTY HOUSE'S STAN CAPTURES ARLINGTON

Chicago, July 31—English Bred Stan, a 5-1 shot owned by Mr. and Mrs. Allie El Reuben of Toledo, Ohio, came from behind Saturday to win the $156,000 Arlington *handicap by a neck over Brush Burn, at 25-1. . . . Stan, given a terrific ride by Eldon Nelson, streaked out of nowhere midway in the stretch and barely went ahead of Brush Burn about 50 yards from the finish.*

From the *Arlington Notebook* by Teddy Cox:

Several days ago, we saw a good piece of horsemanship on the part of the Ponca City, Oklahoma, jockey Eldon Nelson. It seemed that he was definitely beaten when he switched his whip from the right to the left side by the expedient of at first placing the bat in his teeth and then grabbing it with his left hand. The horse won. . . .

It was Eldon's biggest career win. He told Betty, "I'm sending a check to Mom and Dad so they can pay off their place." The next day, Eldon wrote out a check and enclosed a short note, saying, "Dear Mom and Dad, I've come a long way from my first horserace and purse. Take this money and pay off your place. Maybe there will be enough left over to buy a couple of chickens."

And the story of Stan and Eldon did not end that summer. Eldon won five straight races on Stan, including the Arlington Handicap, the Laurel Turf Cup Handicap, and the Meadowland Handicap. The unknown, English-bred horse who fell down and took Eldon through the hedge on their first race, ended up being the fastest grass horse the bush track rider ever mounted.

Long Shot Nelson

For the next 20 years, life for the Nelsons revolved around the East Coast racetracks. The shuffle from Pimlico to Bowie to Delaware to Saratoga, and then a few treasured weeks at home on the cattle ranch in Kansas, became the accepted family routine.

Eldonna and Glen Eldon, Jr. received their education in Catholic schools. The disruption to their kids' lives caused by the frequent moves and changes of school worried Eldon and Betty at first. After talking to other race trackers, they learned that many of the jockeys enrolled their kids in Catholic schools because they all used the same textbooks, making the adjustment easier between schools.

The family outgrew their first travel trailer, and Eldon upgraded to a bigger rig. Their home on wheels went with them everywhere except New York. In Saratoga and Long Island it cost too much to park a trailer, and there were too many restrictions. So, for those meets Eldon rented a house or an apartment. In late fall, when most other riders traveled to the Florida circuit, Eldon took his family home to Cedar Vale, Kansas, and his beloved cattle ranch.

Eldon's reputation for "shunning" the tracks in winter and returning to his ranch caught the eye of many a newspaper columnist. Much was written about how the Oklahoma-born rider's winter layoffs would play havoc with his talent and lessen his chances of getting top-flight mounts, but Eldon ignored the speculation and continued to retreat with his family for a few cherished months of privacy on the ranch.

When Eldon left the racing circuit and decided to retire in 1950, he weighed in at 98 pounds and was too light to have the stamina needed for the daily grind of racing. When he returned in 1953, he weighed 108 pounds and his services quickly were in demand. The other factor that played into Eldon's growing popularity was his ability to rate his mounts down the stretch, then settle them down into a dramatic finish.

Over the years, the annual winter trips back to Kansas almost seemed to boost Eldon's talent and enhance his opportunities. He rode for such notables including W. Haynes, Calumet Farms, Willie Dupont, Elizabeth Arden, and Christiana Stables.

Left to right, Mrs. Harry Lunger, jockey Eldon Nelson, trainer Henry Clark, Mrs. Richard C. DuPont, and Harry Lunger. Mrs. DuPont presented the victory trophy to her cousin, Mrs. Harry Lunger, for Smart's victory at the Gallant Fox Handicap. Smart was owned by Mr. and Mrs. Lunger.

In a *Miami Herald* Sunday edition from January of 1954, the headline read: TIDEWATER SURGES TO $103 INAUGURAL WIN. Beneath a picture of the horses coming into the stretch is the caption: "Hialeah's record Inaugural field bunches up into the stretch turn in a vain attempt to catch the incoming Tidewater." Among three pictures displayed on the full-page spread is one of a smiling Eldon Nelson in the winner's circle, holding the trophy with owner Abe Levinson.

Tidewater, a 50-1 long shot, paid $103 for a $2 ticket. The Inaugural first prize paid $15,950.

The Baltimore Sun from Wednesday, May 5, 1954, proclaimed: JOCKEY NELSON RIDES FOUR WINNERS ON BOWIE PROGRAM. Writer William Boniface reported: "Jockey Eldon Nelson starred on a featureless program here today when he rode four winners—Our Hespers, Texan Sigh, Trout Fly and Iforn—to increase his score for the 19-day meeting to 23 victories. He's one winner behind Nick Shuk in the saddle race of the Bowie session."

In the *Daily Racing Form*, from Friday, September 24, 1954, in the "Hawthorne Notebook" the headline read: CLOSE JOCKEY RACE AT HAWTHORNE; ELDON NELSON RETURNING TO ACTION. In the accompanying article, J.J. Murphy wrote:

> With 13 days of Hawthorne's autumn session already completed, a group of riders are staging a merry battle for the leadership in that division. Grouped well up are senior, Adams, Brooks, Heckmann, Kirkland, Erb, Baldwin and Wickel. Returning from a four-day vacation at his Kansas ranch is Eldon Nelson, the leader at Washington Park, and in several respects the riding star of the present season. . . . Nelson is almost certain to pick up, as agent Danny McAuliffe has some good mounts booked for him this weekend.

Headlines proclaiming the feats of the Oklahoma bush track rider ebbed and flowed for a decade:

The Baltimore Sun on Friday, May 25, 1956 read: NELSON EARNS TOP RIDING HONORS FOR PROGRAM WITH FOUR WINNERS. "With Willie Hartack in New Jersey and Nick Shuk sharing his saddle talent between Pimlico and Garden State Park, Nelson has taken over as Maryland's top reins man. Yesterday afternoon's fine work gave Nelson a score of 17 wins for the meeting."

On the front page of the *Monmouth Park Bugle*, Saturday, July 14, 1956, is a picture of an aging gentleman with the following caption: "DEAN OF TRAINERS . . . Sunny Jim Fitzsimmons today sent Leslie Comb's Nashua, world's greatest money-winning performer, out for another try at the big money in the Monmouth Handicap."

On the next page of the same paper is a smiling Eldon Nelson under the headline JOCKEY SNAPSHOTS. The half-page article tells of Eldon's early beginnings in Oklahoma in match racing and the bush tracks, his retirement in 1950, and his return to horse racing. Writer Jim Raftery ends the article with: "He has won many friends in racing and is popular with horsemen and fans alike. There is an often-used expression on the turf, that 'class will tell,' and those who know Eldon Nelson know he has that 'touch of class.'"

By one of life's twists of fate, Eldon, who had retired and sold his saddle just two years before, was well on his way to fame while Clayton Epperson, "Little Epp," who had ridden hundreds of races in Eldon's old saddle on the Oklahoma bush tracks and once stood with Sunny Jim, the "Dean of Trainers," admiring the colt Nashua, had by then met and married his wife, and given up his dream of becoming a jockey.

Eldon's sister, Evelyn, usually was very efficient at providing the hometown newspaper with the latest news on her brother's riding accolades. On Sunday, June 16, 1957, the Ponca City News proudly declared: LOCAL BOY SECOND AT BELMONT. "Eldon Nelson, former Ponca Citian turned jockey, today came in for second place and $20,000 in the Belmont Stakes at New York."

In that race, Eldon proved to the world he could ride with the best. The crowd expected to see a close match between Galant Man, ridden by Willie Shoemaker, and Bold Ruler, ridden by Eddie Arcaro. What they did not expect was for an Oklahoma bush track rider on a little-known horse named Inside Tract to jump into the race on the final turn and take second money. Shoemaker and Gallant Man took first, while Eddie Arcaro and Bold Ruler, who ran fourth in Kentucky and beat Derby winner Iron Liege in the Preakness, had to settle for third money.

Later that summer, in August 1957, Eldon caused an upset in Saratoga Springs, New York, when he rode Here and There, owned by the King Ranch and trained by Max Hirsch, to a 20-length victory over the favored Miss Blue Jay. The purse for the 77th running of the Alabama Stakes was $29,500. Here and There paid $34.70 to her followers. Eldon, along with the King Ranch and Hirsch, later were stunned when the filly was destroyed in a racetrack stable fire the day after that victory.

Two weeks later, Eldon rode five out of six mounts to victory at Delaware Park, tying Bill Hartack's record set in June of 1955. Later that month, he piloted six straight winners for the all-time mark at Delaware Park, and he equaled the mile track record on Tempted. In July he won the rich $160,562 Delaware Handicap by a nose aboard an 11-1 outsider named Endine.

Eldon Nelson aiming at the "6" ball to commemorate his new Delaware Park record of six consecutive wins. Although matched, the record never has been broken despite more races currently being run per day.

Most bystanders did not know that Bob Ussery, riding the second-place horse Dotted Line that day in the Delaware Handicap, was an Oklahoma boy who had competed many times against Clayton Epperson and Charlie Burr in the bushes. Ussery also would leave his mark in racing history.

On Wednesday, November 5, 1959, in a race too close to call, Eldon outrode Shoemaker and Arcaro to win the $50,000-added Roamer Handicap. Gene Ward broadcast news of the race:

> *... BUT WHAT A RACE IT WAS. Eddie Arcaro, rating the Chenery-owned charger brilliantly behind the trail-blazing of the Shoemaker ridden Demobilize, bided his time in fourth position until halfway through the home-curve of the mile-and-sixteenths test. And then he turned First Landing loose.*

Rounding into the stretch, he was second to the now fading Demobilize, and then Chenery's famed blue silks with the white blocks had the lead by a half-length with only an eighth of a mile to go.

But Eldon Nelson, a vastly underrated reins man by the way, had made his move with Polylad at almost the same moment back on the bend. The three-year-old son of Polynesian, packing 112 to First Landing's 123, was flying on the outside. At the 16th pole, he pulled alongside but lost the lead to First Landing's courageous rally along the rail. Then Polylad unleashed his own finishing kick for the $36,645 victor's swag—more money, incidentally, than he had won in his entire career.

In the press box, the vote was split down the middle on the finish, half of the writers certain First Landing had won, and the other half just as sure it was Polylad. . . . But the big ride was Nelson's on Polylad.

Another big race for Eldon in 1959 was his victory on Tempted in the $36,000 Ladies Handicap at Aqueduct. Tempted, Mrs. Elizabeth DuPont's Mooring Stable filly, broke the record with a time of 2:09 for a mile and five-sixteenths set in 1908 by Ballot at 2:09 and 3-5. With Eldon on board, Tempted had the odds-on choice, Wheatley's High Bid, by two and three-quarter lengths at the line.

Eldon rode Tempted to victory at the Jeanne D'Ar, Beldame, the Jersey Belle Handicap, the Diana Handicap, the New Castle Handicap, and the Maskette Handicap. When Eldon retired from racing, Elizabeth DuPont penned a beautiful letter of thanks to Eldon for his years of dedication and loyalty to her stable.

In Saratoga Springs, New York, in August 1959, Eldon set a track record for 7 furlongs with a time of 1:22 4-5 on a refugee from the claiming ranks named Tom Thumb. Mrs. Edward Lipari claimed the horse for $7,000 and then picked up a purse of $18,680. Eldon took Tom Thumb in first by seven lengths and the horse paid $23.30.

In 1958 and 1959, the Eldon Nelson name was splashed across the front page of every sports page of every major newspaper in the United States. Though pictured with celebrities and beauty queens, Eldon took winning in stride and did not let the glory days change him in any way. He continued to be a loner and a solid family man who worked hard, entertained himself between races with a game of solitaire, and looked forward to the winter when he could return to his Kansas ranch.

After Eldon's return to the track in 1954, he finally had the opportunity to meet the fellow bush track rider he had read about in the Arkansas City newspaper. Charlie Burr, who had taken the Leading Rider in the Nation title in 1952, soon became a friend and a competitor.

The Baltimore Sun, on Thursday, July 18, 1963, noted in a headline: JOCKEYS NELSON, BURR BOTH RIDE "TRIPLES" ON PROGRAM.

Many times over the next 10 years, Eldon and Charlie's paths crossed as they worked their way through the world of racing. Ironically, even though the two jockeys rode together for years, Eldon's wife, Betty, and Charlie's wife, Mildred, did not become friends until many years after both riders had retired. It was Betty who picked up the phone one day in Cedar Vale, Kansas, in the late 1980s and called Mildred in Arkansas City to see if she and Eldon could visit Charlie. Eldon and Betty became regular visitors to the Burr home in those later years.

Eldon continued to make headlines, ride the great horses, and outride some of the greatest jockeys. In 1964, Eldon won out over Ron Turcotte who was astride the favorite, Dedimoud.

Eldon made the racing news in 1965 when he rode 81-1 long shot Bold Bidder to victory in the Jerome Handicap. The 3-year-old Bold Ruler colt had won only three times in 12 starts and was beaten by 55 lengths in the Belmont Stakes. No one expected him to outrun the highly favored 9-5 Cornish Prince or Hirsch Jacobs's entry of Flag Raiser and Turn to Reason.

From *The Blood Horse,* September 25, 1965, p.2355. by William H. Rudy:

WINNER OF THE JEROME: STAKES WINNER NO. 22 FOR BOLD RULER.

Eldon Nelson, who has scored several notable stakes wins at big odds this year, had Bold Bidder off well, running in the rear division but never far off the pace. Flag Raiser took a short lead until Cornish Prince, right with him, managed to slip through on the rail. The favorite had a four-length lead as they went into the turn.

Beaupy, Turn to Reason, and Staunchness were prominent for a time, then Pass the Word made a move, but Cornish Prince appeared in no danger from any of them. It was Bold Bidder, taken down to the rail on the turn and then to the outside of the leader in the stretch, which furnished the only contention.

At the eighth pole it appeared he could not make it, but Cornish Prince, after a fast three-quarters in 1:09 & 3/5, tired badly and in the last couple of strides Bold Bidder passed him for a neck victory. It was four lengths back to the next horse, 17-1 Slystitch.

On October 6, 1965, Eldon rode Advocator to victory in the $78,875 Cowdin Stakes. A 25-1 long shot, Advocator paid $54.40 for a $2 ticket. Pete Axthelm in the Thursday, October 7, 1965, *New York Herald Tribune* wrote: "Nelson is a 39-year-old journeyman rider who is enjoying one of the best years of his long career. He won stakes with Cordially, Smart and Nashandy earlier this summer, and he has recently won two stakes with Bold Bidder. Most of his winners have been long shots. So was Advocator."

In 1971, an unknown Laurel, Maryland, reporter caught Eldon in the jockey's lounge playing a game of solitaire and asked him what kind of a year he was having. The 44-year-old, graying bush track rider replied, "I won the Campbell last spring with Bushido, took a division of the Delaware Valley with Leematt before he was sidelined, and then won a division of the Hawthorne Juvenile with Bee Bee Bee," and added with a smile, "not bad for an old man."

It seems somehow prophetic that a man known for sneaking across the finish line on little-known horses and causing major upsets in big races would wrap up his career by spoiling the Triple Crown bid of Riva Ridge.

On May 20, 1972, Long Shot Nelson rode Bee Bee Bee through the mud and won the Preakness, upsetting Riva Ridge who had won the Kentucky Derby and went on to win the Belmont.

Eldon in the win circle after the 97th running of the Preakness. The tower in the background is about to be painted with the colors of William S. Farish, the owner of Bee Bee Bee.

Bee Bee Bee's upset of the favorite Riva Ridge at the 1972 Preakness yielded the fourth-highest payout in racing history at Pimlico Race Course in Maryland.

Riva Ridge was expected to win the Preakness in 1972. He had romped over the Kentucky Derby field by 11 lengths two weeks earlier. Later, he would win the Belmont with the same ease. Also in the field that day was Key to the Mint, who became champion 3-year-old, and an incredible closer named No Lee Hace.

But on a rainy, dark day in Baltimore, Eldon, now only one year away from hanging up his tack and on a horse who loved the mud, paid lucky bettors $39.40 for a $2 bet, one of the highest payoffs in Preakness history.

Eldon had ridden and won on Bee Bee Bee twice—once in 1971 in the Haw-thorne Juvenile then in 1972 in the Patriot. But he rode him in the Flamingo Stakes and took third, and two other times as a 2-year-old in Maryland on grass where the colt did not do very well.

The morning of the Preakness, Eldon spoke with trainer Del Carroll, who wanted to pull Bee Bee Bee out of the race. There had been a heavy overnight rain and the morning dawned to light rain and dark, threatening skies.

Carroll considered scratching Bee Bee Bee that stormy morning, and when Eldon heard the trainer mention the $10,000 entry fee, he spoke up.

"I'll loan you $5,000," Eldon told Carroll, grinning. "That colt loves the mud."

Eldon certainly was not afraid of the mud. He broke his maiden in the mud way back in 1948. He won the Derby trial on Black George in 1950 in what one reporter called "a seagoing track." He had brought in many a long shot over the years in the slop and in more than a dozen stakes races, stood in the win circle dripping and smiling broadly, his white teeth gleaming through the mud-splatter.

In 1972, Eldon received his biggest win on a long shot in the mud. With the St. Christopher his mother had given him tucked in his skullcap and his lucky silver dollar in his pocket, he had a special feeling that afternoon.

Eldon took Bee Bee Bee to the front right out of the gate. Turning toward home, almost everyone expected Eldon's mount to fade and the heavy favorite, Riva Ridge, to make his move. But instead, Bee Bee Bee lengthened his stride.

On the nationwide CBS telecast, race caller Chick Anderson is heard with a touch of astonishment in his voice, saying, "Bee Bee Bee is drawing away," as the colt increased his lead to four lengths.

After the race, Nelson was quoted: "The Preakness went exactly the way we planned. We went to the front right out of the gate, and went to the turn kicking mud in everybody's face. Most horses don't like that, you know."

In 1973, winding up his career at 46 years of age, Eldon won the $28,500 Endine Handicap for fillies and mares at Delaware Park aboard Christian Stable's Light Hearted, for trainer Henry Clark. Her time was 1:10, one second over Hannibal's 1952 track mark. That feature race was named after Endine, the 11-1 outsider ridden to victory 15 years before by then-31-year-old Eldon Nelson.

Eldon's reputation for bringing in the long shots was written about in 1965 after he rode Advocator to victory in the Cowdin Stakes: "Nelson, who has no superior with come-from-behind horses and avoids the fatal mistake of some more famous jockeys

THE DELAWARE OAKS

CHRISTIANA STABLES-OWNER $50,000 ADDED
HENRY S.CLARK-TR. LIGHT HEARTED
1 1/8 MILE 1:49:3
DELAWARE PARK   JULY 16,1972

ELDON NELSON - UP
WANDA   2ND
JUMP SEAT   3RD

Toward the end of his career, Eldon rode Light Hearted to victory in the Delaware Oaks and later in the Endine Handicap.

of holding their mounts back behind a slow pace, rates the name "Longshot" for his stakes scores on Cordially, $40 in Delaware's Rosenna; Nashandy, $20.20 in Saratoga's Seneca, and Bold Bidder, $164.20 in the Jerome here, as well as that on Advocator."

And that reporter barely scratched the surface of Eldon's long-shot career. There was Tidewater in 1954, a 50-1 shot that paid $103 for a $2 ticket. In 1959 a 10-1

Polylad paid $23.10, and Advocator in 1965, a 25-1, shot paid $54.40.

Few people knew that Eldon's ability to bring in those long shots was directly connected to his work ethic. While many riders would be out on the town after a day's work on the track, Eldon would be watching films and studying horses he was asked to ride. If they had lost in previous races, he wanted to know why. Did they lug in around the turn or get a slow start out of the gate? Did they react to the whip better on the left than the right? Did they have a particular fault he might be able to correct? By studying those films, he was often able to pinpoint and correct a horse's weakness.

That level of commitment and professionalism was rare among riders. In an article by Frank Graham, Eldon was asked, "When you were an apprentice, was there any leading jockey that you especially admired for his style of riding or for any other qualities he had?"

"Steve Brooks," Eldon replied. "He was the most conscientious and hardest-working of any of the riders. He thought nothing of working horses for hours in the morning, and then going out and riding seven or eight races in the afternoon. I thought that was wonderful for a rider of his reputation."

A newspaper article by William Boniface quotes Delaware Park official Jack O'Hara as saying about Eldon, "I don't know what he is to the public, but he is a dreamboat to the clerk of the scales."

O'Hara, who was in charge of the jockeys from the time they made weight at noon until they finished riding for the day, knew the riders' habits, strengths and weaknesses.

"Nelson is the greatest," Jack said. "He never gives me any trouble. He's always on time. Keeps his weight at an even 110 pounds, and talks like a gentleman while never raising or lowering his voice."

That impression of Eldon's character seemed to be shared by other riders, grooms, and track officials during his 26-year racing career. His dedication to hard work and his commitment to excellence followed him from the racetrack to his ranch after retirement. Eldon won the Soil Conservation Award in Sedan, Kansas, in 1992 for building terraces on his ranch in order to fill a pond within two years. He bred and raised prime Angus beef and maintained the 500-acre working ranch near Cedar Vale until he was 85.

During his career, Eldon had 14,452 mounts; 1,928 wins; 1,653 seconds; 1,575 thirds; and total earnings of $10,084,327.

According to a small note in The Blood Horse, when Eldon retired, Laurel Park named the October 29th sixth race the Eldon Nelson Purse in his honor.

Eldon Nelson on the inside rail, right, at Laurel Park in Laurel, Maryland. The photographer who took the photo from below the rail at Clubhouse Turn was banned from the park because of the danger he created to the horses and riders.

Trophies and accolades of every description filled Eldon's ranch house with the proof of many years of hard work and dedication to racing. On one wall in Eldon's study hung the print of a dead heat that came from the clubhouse at Belmont Park. Eldon is on the inside of the picture, Bill Bolanda is seen in the middle, and Ismal Venezuela is on the outside in the three-horse dead heat. The picture gave the admirer a glimpse of the passion of the jockey's competitive spirit and a brief insight into the glory of riding a winner across the finish line. Today, Nelson's trophies and images are on display outside Silks Restaurant at Remington Park in Oklahoma City.

Christiana Stable's yellow and purple silks hung proudly on the opposite wall, sharing space with two caricatures of Eldon by the famous racing illustrator Pierre Bellocq, better known as "Peb." One is of Eldon on Coaltown, with a running clock and the title: "Coaltown World Record Equalized."

Several win pictures graced the walls of the study. An enlarged, framed copy of the Preakness Program from 1972 shows page 8, the 9th race for a mile and three-sixteenths with Eldon Nelson aboard Bee Bee Bee.

In 1989, Eldon was diagnosed with the disabling muscle and nerve disease Myasthena-Gravis. He was quoted in 1992 as saying, "I was so depressed early on, but Betty kept after me and got me out of the depression. She's been wonderful." With Betty's help, Eldon beat the odds and the disease temporarily went into remission. But in 2005, Eldon lost his life's companion of 56 years and began perhaps his hardest race, the challenge of loneliness.

On February 14, 1949, Eldon Nelson rode Coaltown to match the world record and set a new track record at Hialeah Park Race Track in Hialeah, Florida, when he was only 22.

At the age of 82, Eldon still lived on his ranch near Cedar Vale with his dog and a couple of horses. His daughter, Eldonna, kept track of his medical needs, visited every weekend and talked to him every day. Eldonna's husband, Randy, helped with a variety of chores around the ranch, and Eldon's grown grandsons pitched in. The family worked hard to keep Eldon's beloved ranch up and running.

Eldon still enjoyed watching horse races. He had HR TV, as well as TVG, so he could get all of the United States and international races. Just like Charlie Burr and Clayton Epperson, separation from the track never erased his passion for the sport.

In late March of 2008, during the writing of this book, Eldon met Clayton Epperson for the first time. In April, Eldon joined Clayton at Charlie Burr's bedside in Arkansas City, Kansas, with two former lady bush track riders, Lucille Carlile Herber and Jeanette Barnes Gladd, to reminisce. On September 16, 2008, shortly after his life's story had been recorded, Charlie Burr passed away.

Among the many horsemen and retired riders at Charlie's funeral were his forever friends, Lil Epp and Longshot Nelson.

On May 16, 2009, Glen Eldon Nelson was the third rider to be inducted into the Oklahoma Horse Racing Hall of Fame at Remington Park in Oklahoma City.

SOME OF THESE STATISTICS WERE PROVIDED BY
Allan Carter, Historian for
THE NATIONAL RACING MUSEUM

Eldon Nelson's statistics:

Year	Mts.	1st	2nd	3rd	$Won
1946	23	2	2	3	NA
1947	66	2	3	1	NA
1948	645	66	72	78	202,239
1949	703	110	73	81	297,937
1950	494	59	66	53	224,715
1951	23	1	5	2	NA
1952	5	1	1	1	NA
1953	489	62	61	64	207,650
1954	928	164	112	109	686,283
1955	957	101	103	109	352,049
1956	848	146	127	88	491,825

1957	696	101	86	63	627,161
1958	775	126	97	76	664,125
1959	654	73	65	88	552,200
1960	682	70	57	75	402,347
1961	464	41	41	43	205,911
1962	584	43	55	61	284,049
1963	651	88	65	59	412,489
1964	719	78	93	79	471,645
1965	510	74	58	53	570,091
1966	460	54	48	44	256,248
1967	343	31	26	30	171,529
1968	507	59	57	41	284,543
1969	779	120	115	95	608,539
1970	558	87	69	79	524,047
1971	399	60	60	49	492,706
1972	358	62	46	31	680,430
1973	212	42	30	27	413,953

AMONG HIS STAKES WINS ARE THE FOLLOWING:

Alabama 1957 Here and There (King Ranch)
American Legion Hcp. 1957 Ricci Tavi
Arlington Matron Hcp. 1950 Lithe
Arlington Hcp. 1954 Stan
Bed o' Roses Hcp. 1959 Big Effort
Beldame 1959 Tempted
Benjamin Franklin Hcp. 1965 Bold Bidder
Beverly Hcp. 1950 Lithe
Blue Hen 1963 Katie Kitten
Brooklyn Hcp.1957 Portersville
Capitol Hcp. 1956 Weal or Woe
Congressional Hcp. 1969 (2nd div.) Lesju
Conniver Hcp. 1972 Lead Me On
Cowdin 1965 Advocator
Delaware Hcp. 1958 Endine
Delaware Oaks 1972 Light Hearted

Delaware Valley Hcp. 1971 (1st div.) Leematt
Diana Hcp. 1959, 1960 Tempted
Dixie Hcp. 1957 Akbar Khan
Dover 1960 Kisco Kid
Dwyer Hcp. 1962 Cyane (Christiana)
Fall Highweight Hcp. 1957 Itobe
Gallant Fox Hcp. 1964 Smart
Grand Union Hotel 1957 Jimmer
Hawthorne Juvenile 1949 Roman Bath, 1971 (1st div.) Bee Bee Bee
Hempstead Hcp. (1973)
Jeanne D'Arc 1957 Tempted
Jerome Hcp. (1965)
Jersey Belle Hcp. 1958 Tempted: 1960 Undulation
Jockey Club of Buenos Aires [Laurel] 1972 (1st div.) Fernande
John B. Campbell Hcp. 1971 Bushido
John R. Macomber Memorial Hcp. 1957 Akbar Khan
Kentucky Derby Trial 1950 Black George
Ladies Hcp. 1958 Endine, 1959 Tempted
Laurel Turf Cup Hcp. 1954 Stan
Leonard Richards 1956 Ricci Tavi
Manhattan Hcp. 1963 Smart
Maryland Futurity 1954 Best Contract, 1963 Hussar; 1964 (1st div.)
Jackie Dare 1966 Viking Dancer
Maskette Hcp. 1960 Tempted, 1973 Light Hearted
Massachusetts Hcp. 1964, 1965 Smart
Matron Hcp. 1950 Lithe
Meadowland Hcp. [Washington Park] 1954 Stan
Midwest Hcp. 1948 Delegate
Molly Pitcher Hcp. 1970 Double Ripple (1973)
Monumental Hcp. 1971 Lead Me On
Nassau County Hcp. 1959 Endine
New Castle 1959 Tempted
New York Breeder's Cup Hcp. (1960) Open Fire, 1972 Monolith (Michael G. Phipps)
Patriot 1972 Bee Bee Bee
Pimlico 1972 Peabody

Preakness 1972 Bee Bee Bee
Princeton 1966 Politely
Riggs Hcp. 1964 Mr. Steu
Roamer Hcp. 1959 Polylad
Rosenna 1965 Cordially
Royal Poincianna Hcp. 1948 Delegate
Seneca Hcp. 1965 Nashandy
Southern Maryland Hcp. 1970 Red Monk
Survivor Stakes 1972 Bee Bee Bee
The Vagrancy 1958 Outerspace (Mrs. G.S. Smith)
Toboggan Hcp. 1972 Leematt
Turf Cup Handicap 1954 Stan
Valley Forge Hcp. 1964 Smart
Vosburgh Hcp. 1960 Mail Order
Whimsical Stakes (1960) 1969-Double Ripple
World's Playground 1970 Lematt

American Classic Race Wins:
   Preakness Stakes (1972)

Significant Horses
   Coaltown, Silver Spoon, Tempted, Bold Bidder, Bee Bee Bee

CHAPTER 4

Oklahoma Pioneer Jockeys

The following is a partial list of other pioneer jockeys from Oklahoma who blazed a trail through the wilderness of the bush track era:

Oscar Earl "Rabbit" Wells, 1930–1996

Oscar Earl Wells, known to everyone as "Rabbit," rode the bush tracks of northern Oklahoma from 1943–1948. Raised in the hills of Osage County, Oklahoma, southeast of Ponca City, Rabbit was the younger brother of five older sisters. Young Rabbit dropped out of school in the eighth grade to help support his family, going to work for Walter and Guy Shultz at their ranch in Marland, Oklahoma. There, Rabbit, age 13, rode horses for room and board.

Rabbit grew up quickly, gaining a reputation for being a tough competitor on the bush tracks. He was well liked. He received the nickname Rabbit from the Shultz brothers because of his speed and agility.

Rabbit Wells won his first official race on a recognized track on June 10, 1948, at Ak-Sar-Ben Race Track in Omaha, Nebraska. As an apprentice that year, Rabbit broke the track record at Ak-Sar-Ben riding Memphis Bud for five furlongs in the time of 58 2-5 seconds.

In 1949, Rabbit was leading rider at Ak-Sar-Ben. He earned $43,899 that year, his greatest earnings for a one-year period. He celebrated his success by paying cash for a new Mercury. In 1962, one of the last years he rode, Rabbit won the first nationwide race for Appaloosa horses, held in Albuquerque, New Mexico, riding Cheetah's War Chant 350 yards to victory.

Oscar Earl Wells married Katherine Frances Corbett on January 19, 1958. Because of Rabbit's reputation for drinking and his wild behavior, there was a unanimous opinion around the racetrack that the marriage never would last. Oscar and Kathy were married 37 years and had three children: Daniel James, Joyce Ann, and Oscar Earl.

Although Rabbit grew to only 5' 6", he had to constantly lose weight and lived on

```
O-R    Newkirk   4/25/54  WFTF
1-Country Boy Cox  2-Tex McCabe
3-Black Beauty  500yds  SWT-31.2
F Frame-owner      O Wells-up
                            FF
```

Oscar Rabbit Wells winning in April, 1954 at Newkirk on Country Boy Cox owned by Forrest Frame.

Oscar Rabbit Wells up on Kay County Bill, owned by V. L. Payne, in Newkirk.

a diet of Cheerios, steak, tuna fish, and salad. Stubbornly pursuing his dream to ride, he traveled to Arkansas, West Virginia, Illinois, Arizona, Colorado, South Dakota, Ohio, Montana, Florida, Washington, and Kentucky, accepting work anywhere he could find it and never refusing to ride a horse.

TRAINER OF THE MONTH: OSCAR WELLS

Oscar Wells' small stable chalked up a record of 5 starts, two wins, a second and a third to earn this month's honors for their trainer. It took 100% participation by the horses in his barn to accomplish this success. Each of them tallied a win and an in-the-money finish for the owner-trainer. That's right, 6-year old FRIEND LOU and 5-year old BOOTS AND SHOES are the entire stable Wells has in training.

"Of course they're pets," he says of his two runners, "plus they have a job to do." Recently they have been doing it very well.

Wells has been training horses at Fairmount for the past five years. An Oklahoma native, he followed a career as a jockey that took him all over the United States. In 1949 he was the leading rider at Omaha, and for a time he trained horses in Florida. But his wife, Katherine, is St. Louis born and raised, so it was natural for him to settle here.

It allows for a nice working arrangement that is shared by the family. Katherine helps at the track each morning, and a Wells son has a farm in Eureka, Missouri, where the racehorses winter.

It is in Eureka that Wells is grooming a home-bred grandson of Secretariat, and a yearling for which he has high hopes. He has plans for the young stock that he thinks offer "great prospects for next year."

Meanwhile, his two well-bred runners are doing their best to set a winning example for the youngsters.

In the Fairmont Park newsletter an older Oscar Rabbit Wells is honored as Trainer of the Month.

This photo of Oscar Rabbit Wells exercising a horse was on display at the Kentucky Derby Museum in Louisville from August 2011 to April 2012. Included with the photo was a girth Johnny Longden gave Wells in the jock's room in 1947 after a race he won. Oscar's son donated the girth and traveled to Kentucky for the presentation.

Keith Asmussen rode with Rabbit Wells in the bushes. At Park Jefferson in South Dakota in 1959, Rabbit held first place in top jockey standings over Dexter Stanley, who
was tied for second with Asmussen. Keith later was quoted as saying, "I attribute much
of my riding knowledge to an old jockey friend named Oscar Rabbit Wells."

Shortly after his third child was born, Rabbit left his jockey dream behind to
embrace his family responsibilities. He went to work for Ford Motor Company in Hazel-
wood, Missouri, where he remained until he retired in 1989. Throughout his lifetime,
however, even after retirement, Rabbit continued his love for racing by becoming a
successful trainer, owner, and breeder of Thoroughbreds.

Once his children were grown, Oscar immediately returned all of his energy to the
racetrack. In 1990, he passed the requisite trainer's test for the state of Kentucky and
became eligible for his trainer's license. In 1993, three years before his death, Rabbit
was honored at Fairmont Park in Collinsville, Illinois, as Trainer of the Month.

Lucille Carlile Herber, 1931-_____

Born in Enid, Oklahoma, Lucille Carlile grew up riding and training horses for her
father, Perry Carlile, who was known in the mid-1940s as King of the Shetland World.

In junior high school, Lucille rode bareback broncos and bulls in the local rodeos.
After high school, she began training for jeweler Riley Atkinson in Enid, Oklahoma.
Atkinson owned a horse named Ortho's Doughboy, he had purchased the animal at a
Fort Reno government sale and did not receive registration papers. That meant that
even though Doughboy was a Thoroughbred, he could never be raced on a sanctioned
track. But Doughboy was by Hardtack, the sire of Seabiscuit, and quickly proved he
could run. Lucille launched her jockey career in 1949 by winning on Doughboy at Pond
Creek, Oklahoma, going three-quarters of a mile.

Lucille quickly jumped into the jockey arena. At Garfield Downs in Enid, she won
five races in one night in 1950. Then in 1952, she won the derby at the Oklahoma State
Fair on Hustle Gal.

Lucille rode against Clayton Epperson, Charlie Burr, Rabbit Wells, and the Murty
twins, as well as Shirley Barnes, Joyce Riggs, Barbara Berry, and Wantha Davis in Pond
Creek. She rode on a total of 13 tracks in Oklahoma, seven in Kansas, five in Colorado,
two in Wyoming, two in Texas, and one in Nebraska. She exercised, raced, or served as
outrider at Meadowlands, Oaklawn Park, Hawthorn, Sportsman's Park, Ak-Sar-Ben,
Washington Park, Sunland Park, Hollywood Park, and Delmar Race Course.

Lucille married Don Herber in 1951 and raised five children—Paula, Dixie, Donnie,
Ted, and Judy—while traveling on the race circuits. Out of the five, Paula, Dixie, and

LUCILLE HERBER

ROMANS 8:29 *"For whom He foreknew, He also predestined to be conformed to the image of His Son that He might be the firstborn among many brethren."*

The first time I remember about riding I was in the 1st grade: I fell off a Shetland and broke my arm. My father, Perry Carlile, raised Shetlands so that's what I learned to ride and break and even re-broke at times. At about 12 or 13, I began rodeoing and rode Jr. bulls, bareback broncs, pole bending and barrel racing. After graduating from high school I became a jockey and was very successful ... Girls couldn't ride on recognized tracks then so I rode on mile brush tracks in Oklahoma, Kansas, Nebraska, Colorado, Wyoming, Nevada, Missouri, and Illinois. I won over 500 races over the years. After I married my husband Don, who trained and shod, we did the whole works at big tracks across America. We had five children and three were jockeys. I didn't quit ponying and taking jockeys to the starting gates until I was 62. My husband died soon after that and I enrolled in boot and saddle making at Oklahoma State Tech in Okmulgee, Oklahoma. While there, I fell and broke my arm in five places but I kept on going to school and became an artist in tooling leather and painting on leather. God always opens more doors when one closes. While racing, God had me start ministering and having bible studies ... we must "seek first the Kingdom of God and the rest shall be added."

We are an open book before all people ...

PHIL. 2:15 *"that you may become blameless and harmless, children of God without fault in the midst of a crooked and perverse generation, among whom you shine as lights in the world."*

MATTHEW 5:16 *"Let your light so shine before men, that they may see your good works and glorify your Father in heaven."*

I received Jesus when I was 13, but my life changed when I was baptized in the Holy Ghost. Jesus put praise in my heart and tongue, and God gave me a love for all people.

ACTS 17:28 *"for in Him we live and move and have our being"*

He is my everything, He is my all.
He is my everything, both great and small.
He gave His life for me and made everything new,
He is my everything so how about you?

That is part of a song I enjoy because it is true in my life
He is my everything!!!

Lucille Herber of Okmulgee, Oklahoma

Lucille Carlile Herber riding Colorado Mac owned by Floyd Murphy in Liberal, Kansas.

Donnie became jockeys.

Paula was the first to ride at Ellis Park in Kentucky. Dixie rode in Detroit and Louisiana Downs. Donnie in Nebraska and South Dakota. All three learned to ride on the Oklahoma Bush Tracks.

At four months pregnant with Donnie, Lucille won a Powder Puff Derby in Las Vegas. She later told Donnie, "You were actually a jockey before you were born."

The year Lucille and Don got married, they took horses to the Illinois Fair race circuit "because of the money." The purses were $300 in Illinois, compared to $150 in Oklahoma, and the jockey was paid $10 to win. One year in Springfield, Missouri, at the "Little World's Fair," Lucille won the feature race every day with a purse of $500 for each race.

In 1952, Lucille and Don took horses to race in Brush and Denver, Colorado, but Lucille could only gallop because "girls couldn't ride there yet." She did, however, ride at Castle Rock, Holly, Gunnison, Rocky Ford and Greely in Colorado, and in Cheyenne and Laramie, Wyoming. As one of the first pioneer girls on the bush tracks, she earned the much-deserved respect of her male competitors.

She rode in five all-girl races in Greeley, Denver, Las Vegas, Laramie and Sunland Park, winning in all but the Sunland Park race.

Lucille's jockey career ended in 1955 at Sportsman's Park in Phoenix. Mr. Favor, who had set the world's record for 6½ furlongs in 15.2 seconds, ducked out from under her while she was working him one morning, and she took a bad spill. She was unconscious for five days, went through two brain surgeries, and was hospitalized for 30 days. It took a year for her to just get her equilibrium back.

After recuperating from her spill, Lucille trained three Quarter Horses at Turf Paradise in 1956, when they ran a mixed meet of Thoroughbreds and Quarter Horses. She also trained in Juarez, Mexico, in 1972, where daughter Dixie rode for her.

Ordained as a minister in 1984, Lucille immediately began holding Bible-study groups at the racetracks. Carl Nafzger, the trainer who developed three Eclipse Award winners and the 1990 Kentucky Derby Champion, Unbridled, was quoted as saying that the course of his life forever changed after attending one of Lucille's fellowship meetings in Omaha, Nebraska.

Over a period of more than 30 years, Lucille and Don Herber rode and trained horses from coast to coast across the United States. In 1988, when Remington Park opened in Oklahoma City, Don worked as the paddock blacksmith and Lucille served as an outrider. The two were part of the racing community at Remington for many years. Lucille finally retired from the track at age 62.

Three years after losing her husband of 45 years to Alzheimer's, Lucille enrolled at Oklahoma State University in Okmulgee to learn saddle making. Displaying the same pioneer spirit that led her to be one of the first successful women jockeys, today Lucille remains active in church and continues to do her leather tooling.

Shirley Barnes Hunt, 1934-____

Sisters Shirley and Janet Barnes grew up on a farm in Douglas, Kansas. Their father, Wilbur Barnes, always had horses so the sisters developed an early love for riding. Shirley came home from school one day and her father asked her to ride one of his horses, Red Rooster, in a 250-yard match race.

Even though she was a skilled horseback rider and had competed at rodeos and in queen contests, she never had ridden a horse in a race. Wilbur Barnes sensed his daughter's hesitation and encouraged her, telling her she could do it.

Shirley still remembers the thrill of walking into the two-horse gate in the pasture, the intensity of waiting for her father to pull the gate, and the excitement of winning. But probably what caused her to soon give up rodeos and become a jockey was the money. For the first time in her life, she got paid for doing something. She could buy clothes for school!

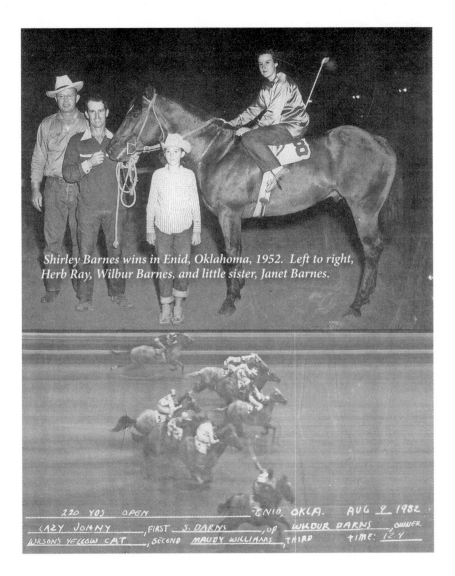

Shirley Barnes wins in Enid, Oklahoma, 1952. Left to right, Herb Ray, Wilbur Barnes, and little sister, Janet Barnes.

220 YDS OPEN _____ ENID, OKLA. AUG 9 1952

LAZY JOHNY _____, FIRST S. BARNS _____, UP WILBUR BARNS _____, OWNER

WILSONS YELLOW CAT ____, SECOND MAUDY WILLIAMS THIRD TIME: 12.4

Early in her career, Shirley rode in moccasins, had no bat, and no skull cap. She quickly developed the skill of getting a horse out of the gate and soon became a force to be reckoned with around the bush tracks of northern Oklahoma and southern Kansas.

A black rider, Alton Lawyer, gave Shirley her first bat. When she asked what she owed him for the bat, Alton replied, "Nothing. I'm givin' that to you so when I outride you there will be no excuses." Many years later, Alton stood with Shirley in Ruidoso, New Mexico, while her oldest son, Billy Hunt, won the All American.

"I wonder where he learned to ride like that?" Alton asked Shirley with a grin.

Shirley rode at Newkirk, Pawhuska, Enid, Stroud, and Woodward.

"The bush track races were pretty wild, but we had good judges and people like

Ben Johnson, Fred Beason, and John Speck to keep things in order. There was no drug testing, of course. One day up at Newkirk, we waited and waited in the paddock for a horse. I asked Daddy, 'Why are they being so slow?' He told me they were probably 'drugging,' but not to worry, that it wouldn't make any difference. Dad was right. We won that race anyway. People knew which owners used drugs, and although the owners weren't banned from racing, they weren't well respected."

Shirley rode against Charlie Burr before and after he went to the East Coast and became leading rider of the nation.

"After he made it big, he'd come back sometimes and ride a race on the bush tracks," Shirley recalled. "They'd hide him before the race. It always aggravated me for the owner to bring in an outside jockey to ride. It wasn't fair. We'd ride the horse and he'd be unbeaten, and then they'd put him in a high-dollar race and tell you they were bringing someone in.

"I'd always torment Charlie Burr when they'd bring him in to ride. I'd go around looking in cars, in the barn, until I found him and say, 'There you are. How come a hot shot like you has to hide?' "

In 1952, Shirley rode her father's horse, Lazy John, in a match race in Meade, Kansas, on a recognized track. Her father negotiated with the track officials for days to get permission for Shirley to ride in that one race. They finally allowed the match race under the condition that the race be run at 8:00 in the morning. Shirley won that first official race riding unbeaten Lazy John against unbeaten Badger's Gray Lady 350 yards for a purse of $5,000.

Wilbur Barnes took black jockey Jackie Myers with them to a track near Jacksonville, Florida, in 1951, but officials there would not let Jackie ride because he was black. Shirley, who grew up in a small Kansas town, had no experience with racial issues, so she did not understand at the time.

Shirley married jockey Willie Hunt in 1953. Willie jockeyed around the Oklahoma bush tracks for years, and later rode in Tucson and Los Alamitos. During the off season he worked construction to support the family. They had three children: Billy, Jimmy, and Sue.

Their oldest son, Billy Hunt, won the triple crown of Quarter Horse racing in 1981 by placing first in the Kansas Futurity, the Rainbow Futurity, and the All American on Special Effort. Jimmy Hunt still rides today at Sallisaw, and Sue trains horses at Blue Ribbon Downs in Sallisaw.

Shirley has cooked for the jockeys at Sunland Park for the past 30 years. Now, at age 75, she's semi-retired, but still enjoys going to the track, visiting with the riders, and being part of the world she has known and loved since childhood.

Janet Barnes Gladd, 1941-_____

The happiest day of Janet Barnes's life was when her older sister, Shirley, got married and her father, Wilbur Barnes, asked her to take Shirley's place riding at the racetrack. Janet was 12 years old and weighed 90 pounds. She, like her sister, started riding with no equipment or license, just a talent to ride.

In a male-dominated environment, Janet thought often about the girls who came before her and paved the way for her to have a chance. The guys she rode with seemed more receptive to her presence because of her older sister's reputation and that of other female jockeys such as Lucille Carlile, Joyce and Nelma Riggs, and, of course, Wantha Davis.

Every girl jockey who ever walked into a starting gate had a dream to become as good as Wantha Davis. The fact that Wantha had defeated the famous Johnny Longdon in an exhibition match race in Mexico in 1949 was probably the single most empowering thought a girl could have when she was the only female rider at the track.

In Janet's seven-year career as a jockey, she rode in Newkirk, Pawhuska, and Heavener, Oklahoma; Orlando and Tropical Park in Florida; and in Kansas.

When Janet was 15 years old, Acan Pappan and Fred Beason put on a meet at Heavener. They needed a good rider and asked Wilbur Barnes if they could take Janet with them for the meet. After Acan promised to get Janet a motel room, feed her, and watch after her, Wilbur consented.

The trip away from home with the two most important men around the racetrack was an exciting adventure for Janet. She won a 350-yard race on Buster Brown, making her dad proud.

By pulling a few strings, Wilbur managed to get Janet in an exhibition race at Tropical Park, Florida, in the mid-1950s. She was the first girl to ever ride on a Florida track. She rode match races in Orlando, Florida, against Terry Lipham, who later became a great rider in the Quarter Horse world.

In 1957, Janet won the 350-yard Newkirk Futurity while riding Silver Creek. She had qualified on a full sister to Paleo Pete, but the owner asked if she would mind if he let Hershel Radford ride the mare in the futurity. Janet rode Silver Creek and won the $150.

Ben Johnson, father of actor Ben Johnson, Jr., was often a judge around the bush tracks of northern Oklahoma. At that time, Ben was foreman of the Chapman Barnard Ranch near Pawhuska. He took a liking to Janet, Shirley, and Wilbur Barnes. One day he handed Janet a thousand-dollar bill and told her to go match her dad's horse Lazy John with another horse. Of course she did not, but the guys got a big laugh at the expression on her face when Ben handed her the bill.

Janet rode until 1960, when she took a bad spill and shattered her ankle. She married horse trainer Frank Gladd in 1963. Because the pair loved the racetrack they centered their lives around training and riding. Wherever Frank trained, Janet exercised horses.

Today, at their ranch near Pawnee, Oklahoma, they board broodmares, break yearlings, and run horses at Remington Race Track in Oklahoma City. Their one son, Wade, helps them with the training and learns from the two people closest to him—two people who have dedicated their entire lives to racing horses in Oklahoma.

Joyce Riggs Church, 1932-_____

Joyce and Nelma Riggs grew up on a farm near Conway Springs, Kansas, riding horses. At 5 years of age, Joyce, along with her two brothers, began to ride her father's horse, King, to school. Her father, William Farris "Doc" Riggs, probably inherited his love of raising and racing horses from his father, who traveled from Missouri to Conway Springs in 1892. Grandfather Riggs raised mules and later horses, stood a stallion,

Joyce Riggs Church wins on Twice Witch, owned by her father Doc Riggs, at Chisholm Trail Park in Pond Creek. COURTESY GENE WILSON & ASSOC. INC.

Joyce Riggs Church wins at Liberal Race Track on Sax Boy, owned by her father, with sister and fellow rider Nelma Jo Ann Riggs.

and participated in pacer races in Conway Springs in the late 1930s.

A quote from a 1953 edition of the Kansas City Star says it all: "On a farm in the wheat lands of South Central Kansas, the W.F. Riggs family has produced a crop unlike that of any of their neighbors—a string of winning race horses and two daughters who ride and train horses."

One of Joyce's most vivid childhood memories is of her father making a trip to Fairfax, Oklahoma, to buy a stallion named Twice and four of his siblings. Joyce and sister Nelma were ecstatic over the new members of the Riggs family.

Over the next several decades, while making a living as a farmer Doc Farris continued to buy, breed, and raise fine Thoroughbred horses. Some of the Riggs horses included: Twice, Twice Witch, Cavalier Trim, Twice Murry, Twice Irv, and Pair Guy. After he retired from farming, Doc Farris had a stable of horses at Sportsman's Park; Hot Springs, Arkansas; Atlantic City; St. Louis; and Turf Paradise.

Joyce's first race was a "lap and tap" race with no starting gate. The two-horse match race on a sandy road allowed the horses to start from a standstill and run down a short straightaway. Similar to the early Oklahoma bush track races, people would congregate in a pasture on Sunday, set up match races, and watch the horses run.

After exercising her father's racehorses for years around the farm and participating in several match races, Joyce began to ask her father to give her a chance to jockey. But it was only after her brother, Marion, became too big to ride that Doc Riggs gave then-12-year-old Joyce permission to compete at a race meet.

In 1946, at 14, Joyce won her first purse race at Ted Yocham Race Track in Wichita, Kansas. A picture from a newspaper clipping about the race shows Joyce standing on the scales holding her saddle and wearing saddle oxford shoes instead of riding boots. Five years later, at 19, Joyce had ridden more than 900 races, taken 450 firsts, and was in the money most of the time.

One of the best horses Joyce remembers from those early days was a gelding named Starlight. She won on Starlight in Enid, Oklahoma, going one-half mile and 70 yards.

Not only was Joyce a good rider, but she quickly gained the respect of the male jockeys and race fans alike. At a meet in Pond Creek when Joyce was just 14, Roy Davis, secretary of the Pond Creek Roundup Club, was quoted as saying, "There was a debate that Joyce got fouled in the feature event during opening day of the meet, but she refused to press any charges—said she didn't notice Little Bob's jockey crowding her on the turn." That ended the debate. Little Bob won the race, and Twice Murry, ridden by Joyce took second. One of the judges at the meet was amazed and said, "That's the first girl jockey I ever saw who wasn't always crying ... that's why they won't let them ride in the big meets."

In 1948, Joyce's notoriety landed her an appearance on the front page of the Coffeyville, Kansas, sports page, and at the Kansas Inter-State Fair that year, Joyce rode in four Thoroughbred races, taking two firsts and two seconds.

Joyce Riggs Church wins the Nebraska Futurity in August, 1951 on Kanzo owned by W. Stuchal, running 330 yards in 18.8.

Doc Riggs was an excellent trainer, so Joyce learned to ride and train from an experienced horseman. As time passed and she sharpened both her riding and training skills, outside owners began asking her to ride and train their horses.

Joyce set a track record for a 330-yard race in Meade, Kansas, riding Kanzo, a filly she broke and trained. The filly was owned by Wilber Stuchall of Douglas, Kansas. Joyce rode Kanzo in the Quarter Horse futurity trials in Meade where she won. In the finals of that futurity, Kanzo ducked over into the turn a little before going on down the straightaway, and it cost her the race.

Joyce also went with Wilber to Nebraska and won on Kanzo in the Nebraska Futurity. Later, when Kanzo was shipped to California to run and Joyce was teaching in California, she went out to the track and galloped Kanzo.

Unlike most of the other jockeys, Joyce did not live the entire bush track experience. William Riggs would haul his horses and daughters to the track, allow them to ride his horses, and then return home. Joyce and Nelma never saw a lot of the drinking, gambling, or the wild side of the racetracks.

Perhaps that is why Joyce eventually began to think in terms of the world beyond horse racing. But, at 19, while a sophomore at Friends University in Wichita, Kansas, and president of the Women's Athletic Association, a member of the band, assistant of women's physical education, and president of Delta Roe Alpha Nu, Joyce still jockeyed in the summer. In a 1951 article by Donna Bolton, Joyce is quoted as saying, "Each summer I say it's the last season, but once you get racing in your blood, it's hard to get it out."

Joyce rode her final purse race at Newkirk, Oklahoma, in 1961, at 29 years of age. She won on Longone, owned by local owner and trainer Dwight Clum. She had ridden War-O-Bart out of Man-O-War for Clum in Nebraska. But, by the early '60s and nearing age 30, Joyce knew her days as a jockey were numbered. It was not just the practicality of continuing to ride, a spiritual tug began to beckon her toward a life of full-time teaching.

Joyce received a bachelor's degree from Friends University and a Master's Degree from Texas Women's University in Denton, Texas. She married Avery Church in 1965 and began her career in teaching. Remaining a dedicated athlete, Joyce taught health and recreation, and physical education. She coached tennis and swimming, and spent her last 25 years teaching special education students on the junior and senior high school level in Kansas.

Joyce competed against Charlie Burr, Clayton Epperson, Rabbit Wells, Lucille Carlile, Betty Bryant, Barbara Berry, and Nelma Riggs. She remembered seeing Wantha Davis once at the track in Wichita, but never competed against her. Just before Charlie

Burr left under contract to go to Fairmont Park, Joyce rode with him in Anthony, Kansas. Joyce remembers Charlie coming over to tell her and the other riders goodbye.

Joyce Riggs Church rode on the following race tracks in Oklahoma: Enid, Kingfisher, Anadarko, Lawton, Woodward, Seiling, Pond Creek, Laverne, and Newkirk. She also rode on 15 tracks in Kansas, as well as tracks in Missouri, Illinois, New Mexico, and Nebraska.

She visited and exercised horses for her father in Atlantic City and at Monmouth Park in New Jersey; Hot Springs, Arkansas; Fairmont Park and Cahokia Downs in Illinois; Turf Paradise in Arizona; and River Downs in Ohio.

Joyce calls Conway Springs, Kansas, home today. In the spirit of her father and grandfather, Joyce, after becoming part of this project, began organizing an event for the folks around rural Conway Springs in "Celebration of the Horse."

Nelma Jo Ann Riggs Henderson, 1937-1976

Like her older sister Joyce, Nelma Riggs grew up riding King, the family horse. As early as 4 years old, Nelma bounced behind Joyce on King. By 6, Nelma tagged along with her father and sister to the race meets and watched in awe as her 11-year-old sister began to exercise the powerful racehorses recently purchased by their father, Doc Riggs.

On Saturdays, Nelma loved to ride King from the farm into Conway Springs, Kansas, take kids for rides, and teach them to ride. Nelma loved animals in general. She was known all around Conway Springs as the girl on a horse with a dog. She always had a dog with her, no matter where she went.

The first day Nelma stood with her parents and watched 14-year-old Joyce actually win a horse race at a track in Wichita, Kansas, she yearned to follow in her big sister's footsteps. Nelma soon went to work on her father, saying "Give me a chance."

Doc Riggs finally succumbed to Nelma's relentless demands and gave both Joyce and Nelma two of his young Thoroughbreds. Each girl had the responsibility of their two colts. In the beginning, Joyce would ride the colts and Nelma would ride King to train the colts to break out of the gates and go around the turns. Later, Nelma was permitted to exercise and eventually jockey on her two horses. So at ages 9 and 14, the Riggs sisters, who already were skilled riders, began to train horses under their father's close supervision.

At 10 years old, Nelma was proudly pictured in an article with big sister Joyce. Shoulders drawn back and a stern look of determination on her young face, Nelma seems to be saying, "Look at me. I'm next."

Although the entire article centers around 14-year-old Joyce's riding career, the last paragraph happens to mention Nelma: "In her first season as a rider, with two races she has an even split—one win, one loss."

While the sisters were protected to a great extent from the outside world, they could not be sheltered from the realities of life. In 1949, on an ordinary day at the racetrack while Joyce was riding King and Nelma rode beside on another horse, King suddenly fell to his knees. The 22-year-old faithful family horse regained his feet only to take a few steps and fall again with a painful cry neither girl would ever forget. King died before their eyes.

Probably in an attempt to help her young daughters, and all of the neighborhood children, say goodbye to their beloved friend Vera Riggs put an obituary in the *Conway Springs Star*.

OLD KING SERVED LONG AND WELL

Dan Patch and other great racehorses spent their retiring years resting, but not so with Old King, who served to the end.

Old King, 22 years old last month, faithful old horse owned by Farris Riggs, dropped dead last Thursday morning while Joyce Riggs was riding him. He was known and really loved by so many youngsters and many grownups in the community that they feel a fitting obituary is in order. Because of his gentleness and seeming desire to make the youngsters feel at ease while riding him, he gave many their first lessons in horseback riding.

Mrs. Riggs' father, A. B. Olmstead, raised him as a colt and sold him to Farris when 2 years old. Farris raced him at every one of Conway Springs' fall fairs since then and won many events. The Riggs girls, Joyce and Nelma, both now popularly known as riders all over the Midwest in racing circles, learned to ride on Old King, and they have since been riding Thoroughbreds in top racing events in Kansas and surrounding states.

Nelma may have continued to be in Joyce's shadow for many years, but she never gave up her dream to ride. In an article from a 1950 newspaper clipping, a smiling Nelma is pictured in her silks and goggles aboard Easter Boy. The article reads in part: "Thirteen-year-old Conway Springs girl Nelma Riggs booted her mount, Easter Boy, home four lengths ahead of a field of eight horses in the featured four-and-a-half-furlong race at the end of the first day of the Eastern Cowley county fair at Burden, Kansas. The slight, pretty schoolgirl romped across the finish line four lengths ahead of the pack on a leggy sorrel horse named Easter Boy."

Dighton, Kansas
Owner — Clem Clum
Distance — ½ Mile & 70 Yds.
Time —   PAIR SUE
Trainer — Clem Clum
Race —   N. Riggs-up
Date — 11 August 1950

Nelma Jo Ann Riggs Henderson wins in Dighton, Kansas. Sister, Joyce, holding horse and owner/trainer Clem Clum.

In another article during that same time period, taken from the Pond Creek news-paper: "A girl jockey booted home the winner in the feature futurity race Saturday, in the third day of the annual all race meet at Chisholm Trail Park here before 500 fans. The winner, Annalex, owned by France and Sawyer, Watonga, was ridden by Nelma Riggs of Conway Springs, Kansas."

Although Nelma did not ride as much as her older sister, she rode long enough to win against Joyce on one occasion. In Anthony, Kansas, Joyce rode Starlight and Nelma won the race on Miss Campbell going one-half mile and 70 yards. Of course, little sister had to rub the victory in just a little.

Nelma married horseman Max Henderson on May 19, 1957, and continued a life centered around horses and racing for the next 19 years. In the early years of their marriage, the couple had a stable of horses at Hot Springs, Arkansas, and Sportsman's Park, and ran at many of the same tracks as Nelma's father, Doc Riggs. Later, Max worked as a night nurse at the foaling barn at Lowrance Ranch in Claremore, Oklahoma.

One summer, Max and Nelma went to Ohio with a string of horses from Lowrance Ranch.

Max and Nelma had one daughter, Colleen. Nelma would stay home in Purdy, Missouri, so Colleen could remain in the same school while Max went off to the race circuits from mid-February until October. But there were times when the call of the track became too much for Nelma. Sometimes she would take her young daughter off for days at a time to the track. Other times, Colleen visited her grandparents. But Nelma always made sure Colleen kept up her grades and remained in school.

After Colleen graduated from high school, Max and Nelma went back on the race circuit together. One of Nelma's lifetime dreams had been to compete at Churchill Downs in Kentucky. Finally, after 30 years of riding, raising, and training horses, Nelma found herself living that dream. Max and Nelma had been at the meet in Kentucky just long enough for her to ride a few of their horses in the afternoon races, long enough for her dream to come true.

At age 39, Nelma Jo Anne Riggs left this world doing what she lived for, "being in the saddle." Nelma had been through multiple injuries and yet continued to dedicate her life to horse racing. Everyone who is a "race tracker" knows the danger, but to those devoted to the running of horses, the love of the sport erases the risk. In the end, like many riders before her, Nelma made the ultimate sacrifice.

On June 14, 1976, at Churchill Downs, Nelma had begun the morning workout. She crawled up on a cantankerous horse that she had trouble with in the past. On the backside, going into the turn, the horse shied and threw Nelma into the rail, breaking her back and puncturing a lung. She died within hours.

Herman Moore, 1942- _____

One of the few African-American jockeys to ride the bush tracks in the 1950s, Herman Moore grew up on Twelfth Street in Ponca City, Oklahoma, in what was then

Herman Moore riding Leo Deeds to victory in the beginning of his career.

considered "Dixie," the segregated, Negro part of town. Herman's house was almost directly west of the old Ponca City bush track. His uncle had a pair of binoculars, and Herman began to watch men match horses on the half-mile straightaway that ran from old Highway 60, south, down to John Turner's farm.

Herman became more and more mesmerized with the world of horse racing. One evening, he got enough nerve to sneak down and take a closer look. Standing there at

Herman Moore rides to victory in a match race in 1963, in Crosby, Texas. The owner of the horse flew him to Texas for the race, but did not give him time to change his clothes.

the track with no one else around, Herman realized his lifetime dream was to become a rider. He knew it would not be easy for a little black boy from Dixie to mingle in the white man's world, but he was determined to find a way.

He immediately began to slip up on the back of Hug Davis's broodmares when no one else was around. With just a bridle, Herman would sit on the mares and fantasize what it would be like to come out of the nearby two-horse gate astride a real racehorse.

Probably Herman would never have had the nerve to even get on one of Hug's

Herman in the win circle on Lena's Bar in 1960 at Sunland Park in New Mexico. To the left of the horse is Ted Wells with his son, Scott Wells. Scott currently is the manager of Remington Park in Oklahoma City. Standing to the right is Buffalo Wooten, who served as guardian for many bush track boys away from home.

horses if it had not been for Jackie Myers. Jackie, another black rider from Ponca City, was about three years older than Herman. Herman knew from his long-distance observations that Jackie had been riding and exercising horses for Hug for some time.   If Hug gave Jackie a chance, Herman thought Mr. Davis might give him a chance to ride too.

Hug began noticing young Herman hanging around the barn helping Jackie. He probably noticed his horses being mysteriously wet from sweat sometimes in the afternoon. Soon, Hug put Herman to work helping him out around the barns. When

Hug was not around, Herman would sneak a ride anytime he got the chance. It would be several years, but Herman did ride for Hug in Littleton, Colorado, at Centennial.

Herman's love for and dedication to riding soon began to pay off. The first race he rode was a match race in a pasture somewhere south of Ponca City. He won on a horse called Go Lady Go, which may not have been her real name, for Chick Wehrle. Not too long after that, he rode his first "official" race out of a starting gate in Pawhuska, Oklahoma, for Bill Sharp and won on Leo Deeds.

Although racial bias was clearly a factor in his struggle to become a rider, Herman never let it discourage him. To get any horse, he had to be the first one at the track and the last one to leave. He had to work harder than anyone, keep a good attitude, and be excited to accept any mount.

He soon learned that getting the opportunity for the better horses would take time. He was asked to ride the losers, the rogues, and the horses no one else wanted to ride, but that challenge did not stop him.

Even in the '50s, when the lines of black and white were clearly drawn, men respected hard work and dedication. It was not long before Herman began to ride the better horses and opportunities started to open for him. At age 15, he went to Nebraska with a fake ID and rode. At 16, he went with Bill Sharp to Wichita and won two races.

He also won a futurity at Burwell, Nebraska, for Sharp that same summer. In 1959, when Herman was 17, Sharp sent him and a horse to Denver where Bill assigned C.D. "Buffalo" Wooten to be Herman's guardian. Wooten was to make sure Herman went to school and rode Bill's horse in the evenings at Centennial.

From Denver, Herman traveled to California to ride at Los Alamitos, then to Bay Meadows, then back to Los Alamitos. A professional jockey at that time named Henry Page was going to ride a mare named First Call, but he decided to ride another horse so Herman got to ride the mare. On the same day that Vandy's Flash set a record at 17.5 for 350 yards, Herman, riding First Call, ran 350 yards in 17.7. Henry Page's agent came around then and wanted to get Henry on First Call her next out.

It was the first time Herman stood up against injustice. He told Wooten, "If you do that, I'm gone." Buffalo Wooten believed him, because he let Herman continue to ride First Call. By then, owners and trainers had begun to call Herman "Mistro" because of his ability to get up to the finish line just in time to win.

Herman remembers the way it was in those early years.

"Owners would be sitting around at the tracks, bragging, and next thing someone would be saying he had a horse that could outrun anything for 220 yards, a rider would be mentioned, and the race was on."

In 1965, when Herman was 22 and riding in California, he got a call to ride a match race in Crosby, Texas, for 350 yards on a certain filly. He got on an airplane, someone picked him up at the airport, and took him straight to the racetrack. Inside a building near the track was a table with money piled high. Some guy was standing by, watching the money. Kenny Kite, the trainer, had warmed the mare up. They took Herman straight to the gate in a car. He rode the mare, won the race, and was paid $2,500 for winning.

In the win picture, Herman has on dress pants and a white shirt. They did not even give him a chance to change clothes.

One of the greatest horses Herman rode was Rebel Cause, owned by Dale Robertson of Yukon, Oklahoma. Rebel Cause won the $25,000 California Derby at Los Alamitos. Diamond Charge was also one to remember, as was No Butt, a great champion mare. He rode Glory Be Good, who broke Monita's world record of 17.7 for 330 yards. An article in a racing magazine mentioned the owner and trainer, but did not mention Herman as the jockey. He got ribbed about it by the other jockeys, but just grinned and shrugged, saying "Everyone knew who rode that horse."

Herman Moore rode the great Dynago Miss. He rode Lena's Bar by Three Bars, owned by Walter Merrick. Herman won two races on Lena's Bar, who was the dam of Easy Jet, and he won on Go Effortlessly, who was dam of Quarter Horse Triple Crown-winning Special Effort.

Herman remembers a Ponca City man, Russell Burdick, coming to Raton, New Mexico. Russell had no legs, so the controls for his car were on the steering wheel. They would let him drive his car right up in front of the grandstand so he could see the race.

"Tom Searcy was trainer for Russell Burdick," Herman said. "They were partners and they produced some great horses, including Dyna Flow."

Like every rider, Herman had injuries along the way and spent days at a time in a hospital and sometimes months off of horses. He broke a leg twice and an ankle twice.

In the bushes, Herman rode at Newkirk, Enid, Pawhuska, Apache, Fairfax, Stroud, McAlester, and Sallisaw and in Kansas at Burden, Eureka, and Anthony. In his career, he rode in California, New Mexico, Arizona, Louisiana, Missouri, Colorado, Wyoming, Nebraska, South Dakota, Michigan, New York, and Canada.

Some of the great owners and trainers Herman rode for included Walter Merrick, Bud Warren, Gene Chambers, Harriet Peckham, Brandy Culver, Gerald O'Brian, Lloyd Potter, Bill Sharp, Tom Searcy, and the Eppersons.

Herman rode with Joe Thomas, Johnny Grizzard, Harley Crosby, Floyd Campbell, Roy Brooks, Joyce Riggs, and G.R. Carter from the bushes. He rode with, and later for,

Joe Thomas, and with and for fellow friend and African-American rider Tecumseh Starks. He also rode for Paul and Clayton Epperson.

Herman's major wins include:

Rocky Mountain Quarter Horse Association Futurity 1960 .... Heavenly Flower
Rocky Mountain Quarter Horse Association Futurity 1961 .... Miss Bar Leo
California Derby .... Rebel Cause
Texas Futurity .... Laurita Bar
Futurity, Burlington Colorado .... Scianluck
Pueblo, Colorado Derby .... Come on Scooper
Louisiana Derby 1983 .... Hemp Easy Girl

One tragedy surrounding his life as a jockey will remain with Herman forever. In 1962, Jackie Myers, his longtime jockey friend and mentor from Ponca City, committed suicide in the back seat of Herman's car as they were leaving Los Alamitos Race Track. "It's something you never forget," Herman said. "Jackie was a fine rider and a good friend. He was a pioneer to me. He paved the way."

Jackie Myers with Ponca City Blue and O.E. "Hug" Davis, trainer, holding the horse. Jackie started cleaning stalls, and ultimately riding, for Hug Davis at the age of 9.
COURTESY OF LINDA CLARK.

Jackie Myers, 1939-1962

Jackie Myers also was born and raised in "Dixie," the segregated section of Ponca City. He attended Attucks all-black school. When Jackie was 9 years old, Hug Davis of Ponca City began letting him work around his horse barn, which was near the Ponca City Race Track. Young Jackie voiced a desire to ride, so Davis asked Jackie's mother, Vera, for permission to let her young son ride. Subsequently, Jackie rode for Davis for many years around the bush tracks.

Hug Davis's daughter, Linda Clark, said, "Jackie went with us every time we hooked up the horse trailer. Even if Dad wasn't running a horse that weekend, Jackie would go with us and ride horses for other owners."

Jackie Myers won in Newkirk on Kay County Bill owned by Lynn Payne in April, 1955. COURTESY HOLTON PAYNE.

Jackie Myers rode Kay County Bill owned by V.L. Payne to victory in 1956 in the Ben Johnson Memorial. COURTESY HOLTON PAYNE.

According to Linda, Jackie won many races on two of Hug's best horses during that time—Miss Ponca City and Mc It.

Linda recalls an incident at the races in Burden, Kansas, in the early 1950s, when a café owner would not allow Jackie to eat with her and her dad.

"He will have to eat in the kitchen," the owner said.

"Well," Hug replied, "if Jackie has to eat in the kitchen, we'll all eat in the kitchen."

Linda says she still vividly remembers sitting with her father, mother, and Jackie Myers at a small table at the back of the steaming kitchen, with dishes clanking, and cooks and waitresses working around them while they ate in strained silence.

Jackie rode on most of the same tracks and with many of the same owners and trainers as Herman Moore. He also rode for Zeak Walker. He won on Leo Star Lady for Fred Swalley, Vandy's Flash and Connie Reba for Bud Warren, Vanna Var for Dee Garrett, Askew Arkie for Brandy Culver, and rode awhile for John Askew in Arkansas. He won the derby trial on Dynago Miss in Ruidoso.

Tecumseh Starks 1939–2008

Tecumseh "Starky" Starks was another outstanding African-American rider. At age ten, Starky was living with his grandmother in Boynton, Oklahoma, when Gene Jeffries of Stillwater asked if the boy could ride for him. Starky's grandmother allowed her grandson to go live with Mr. Jeffries in Stillwater and so began a jockey career that lasted thirty years.

Starky knew most of the owners and trainers of the early bush track era and rode many times for Jack Baldwin and Putt McCormick. He was a major influence on Floyd Campbell and Herman Moore and a good friend of the Murty twins. He rode with most of the boys from the early to mid-fifties.

Tecumseh "Starky" Starks, upper left corner with other boys from the bushes, including Charley Smith, Herman Moore, and Harley Crosby, in 1959 at Centennial Race Track in Colorado.

MISS STARNES   DEAD HEAT   GRAY BAR
RONALD BANKS, UP   TECUMSEH STARKS, UP.
Winner Fifth Race Dec. 7, 1955. Purse $1200. Los Alamitos Race Course
Guinea Pig Cee (3rd)   (350 yds.-18.7)   Kitten's Ida Red (4th)

OWNER: EARL CARNES   TRAINER: R.L. BANKS

Later, as a professional, Starky worked on all of the major tracks including: Santa Anita, Oak Lawn Park, Ak-Sar Ben, Sunland Park, Ruidoso Downs, and Los Alamitos Race Course. Probably his biggest race was the 1968 Rainbow Derby.

In his late forties, Starky gave up riding. He began breaking and training colts

Tecumseh Starks wins on Rainy Wins in Sunland Park, New Mexico in 1968.

Pawhuska jockeys in 1950 with Tecumseh "Starky" Starks, bottom left, and Wayne and Duane Murty, top left. The Murtys referred to Starky as their best friend. COURTESY WAYNE AND DUANE MURTY.

at Lubbock Downs and continued working with horses until he was 71. He worked closely with general manager Bobby Willis and owner A.C. Arnett. A horse that Starky trained, Big Nine Oh, took second in the All American Futurity. Another horse Starky trained, Time Machine, won The Oklahoma Quarter Horse Derby in 1973 at La Mesa Park in Raton, New Mexico.

In 1980, The Lubbock Digest quoted Starky "I rode more than a thousand races and never took a spill."

Starky's wife, Elaine, knew nothing about horse racing when they married, but she stayed with him and supported him for 38 years. They had two children, Renita and Sissy. One of Starky's sons from a previous marriage, Tecumseh Starks, Jr. became a jockey and was in a win picture at Blue Ribbon Downs in 1995 on Little Sara.

Harley Crosby won the Oklahoma Futurity in Pawhuska in 1958.

Harley Eugene Crosby, 1939–2010

Harley Crosby began his career as a jockey on the Oklahoma bush tracks in 1952. Born in Drumright, Oklahoma, to Tom Sanders and Hattie Louise Davidson Crosby, Harley was the fourth of nine children. He spent his early childhood in a rented rural house west of Tulsa that had no electricity, gas, or running water. The landlord had two old workhorses in the pasture nearby, and Harley started riding them. Soon, his urge to ride turned into an obsession. He began to sneak out and secretly ride neighbors' horses, using a piece of bailing twine to wrap around the horse's nose and riding bareback, Indian style.

*Harley wins at Centennial Race Track in 1959 on Kay County Bill owned by V.L.
Payne.* COURTESY HOLTON PAYNE.

Harley's love for riding took him to the Oklahoma bush tracks, where he rode his
first race in Turley, Oklahoma, at the age of 13. He does not remember if he won the
match race out of the two-horse gate at C.J. "Putt" McCormick's track, but he remembers that the thrill of racing horses became his life that day.

Shortly after Harley's introduction to match races, he met race trainer Emmett
Mosier, who took him under wing. Mosier started putting Harley up on his horses and
letting the youngster gallop them. Ray "Peck" Wasson also played a part in Harley's
early development as a jockey, as he did with Harley's younger brother, Charles "Powell"
Crosby.

It was not long before Harley won his first race on an official bush track in Enid, riding a horse for a father and son, Ray and Jack Baldwin of Derby, Kansas. Shortly after that, he went with a couple from Enid who owned two horses and who followed the fair circuit from Illinois, through Missouri, to Kentucky.

The "Hully Gully" races in Kentucky were similar to what Joyce Riggs from Kansas called "lap and tap." The horses walked up to a starting line and when they were fairly even, the jockeys gave them the go. In Illinois, Harley had a brief experience with mule sulky racing.

Harley got his first license in Springfield, Illinois, at age 15, by claiming he was 16.

The last race Harley won was in 1984 on Fire Away at Blue Ribbon Downs.

He had ridden in match races in Oklahoma for three years by then, and although purses did not exist, heavy betting did. His biggest win was a match race riding Jennie Styles for $1,000.

Like every jockey, Harley soon found that the glory of the win was only one dimension of a jockey's life. At Littleton, Colorado, at age 16, Harley was suspended for a week at Centennial Race Track for an offense he cannot remember. He stayed in the track room and washed dishes that week in order to stay alive until he could get back in the saddle. But he went on to become leading rider four years in a row at Centennial.

In 1958, Harley won the Oklahoma Futurity in Pawhuska, riding Real Silver for Dean Cropp. Real Silver was trained by W.R. "Chick" Wehrle. At 19, he had become a competitive athlete, ready to pursue his dream. And although he struggled making weight his entire career, Harley rode for the bigger part of 30 years.

In the 1960s, Harley followed the circuit that began in California at Los Alamitos Race Course, went to Centennial in Colorado or Raton, New Mexico, to Ruidoso Downs, New Mexico, and then back to California to either Los Alamitos or Bay Meadows. Harley was among the top 10 riders during those years, riding both Thoroughbreds and Quarter Horses to the win circle. Harley's wins include:

The March 5, 2010, *Native American Times* weekly newspaper announced: "The Cherokee Nation has no plans to reopen Blue Ribbon Downs in Sallisaw as a racetrack." Chief Chad Smith said, "The track has proven over the last two decades, under a whole host of owners, that it just can't make its way as a racetrack."

Blue Ribbon Downs began running in the early 1960s, and in 1984 became the state's first track to offer pari-mutuel racing.

Arizona Quarter Horse Futurity	1963	Dick Rillian
Colorado Futurity	1964	Comet Jr.
Colorado Derby	1964	Golden Wiggy
Oklahoma Quarter Horse Derby	1966	Lanovay
APHA Paint Horse Futurity	1972	Party Gal
Rocky Mountain Quarter Horse Association Derby	1973	John's Note

Raton Futurity (First Running)	1962	High Bend
Ruidoso Downs Derby	1964	Chaundell
Los Niños Handicap	1966	Blobby Charger
Senorita Stakes	1967	Custom Jet
Oklahoma Quarter Horse Futurity	1967	Custom Jet
Sun Country Futurity	1969	Jaguar Rocket
All American Congress Futurity	1970	Gold Copy
The Raton Futurity	1974	Angel's Jet Rail
The Raton Derby	1975	Jet Rail
Spring Futurity	1977	Mr. Big Wheel
B.R.D. Yearling Futurity	1977	Sanuva Jet
Garfield Poor Boy Futurity	1979	Favorite Past Time

Harley rode in the All American, the most prestigious Quarter Horse race, four times. Although a win eluded him, he finished eighth on Hygro Leo in 1963, 11th on Peck's Boy in 1964, fourth on Go Rebel Go in 1965, and third on Classy Native in 1981.

Of course, Harley remembers his missed opportunities as well as his triumphs. In 1962 he broke Hustling Man, then went out to California. Hustling Man went on to win the All American that year. In 1967, he was riding Custom Jet owned by Bud Warren and Laico Bird owned by Jim Jones. He gave Custom Jet first call over Laico Bird. Custom Jet got sick and died before the trials. Bobby Harmon rode Laico Bird to victory in the All American.

"Prissy Gold Digger may have been the fastest horse I ever rode," Harley says. Prissy Gold Digger set five track records from Oklahoma to California. Harley won the Kansas Futurity on her in 1977, then came back and won that same race in 1979 on Favorite Past Time.

Harley came from behind on Ye Song to win Oklahoma's first pari-mutuel Thoroughbred race on August 30, 1984, at Blue Ribbon Downs in Sallisaw, Oklahoma. His last futurity win was on December 15, 1984, at Sallisaw aboard Shiloh Reb. The following day, after riding two races at Blue Ribbon Downs, winning one and placing fifth in the other, Harley decided to hang up his tack. It was time to quit riding, but his love for racing would not allow him to retire from the track completely.

Good Eye, Vinegar Bend, Queen Wood, Idle Hour, Idle Time, Suleo, Kay County Bill and F.L. King B are some of the horses Harley remembers from his bush track days. He rode with many of the riders mentioned in this book on the following Oklahoma bush tracks: Anadarko, Ada, Pryor, Claremore's old fair grounds, Miami, McAlester, Enid,

Newkirk, Ponca City, Pawhuska, Fairfax, Stroud, Skiatook, and Sallisaw.

Some of the trainers Harley remembers include Red and Barton Carter, Comer Evens, Jim Brogden, Brownie and Jerry Sanders, Lloyd Phinney, Wilber Barnes, Lucky Ledbetter, Andy and Kay West, John Gunter, Bud Warren, Hugh Arnold, Paul Walter, Sammy Hester, Joe Neff, Dave Newby, Clarence Runyan, Eddie Jiles, Don and Ray Tackett, Lee and Bud Gladd, Paul and Cleo Harlow, Bob-Billy and Connie Burress, Jack Reany, Larry Sharp Olin and Opal Leonard, Henry Orth, and Sam Bryson.

Since retiring in 1985, Harley has served as an Oklahoma non-pari-mutuel steward, a pari-mutuel steward, an associate judge, Blue Ribbon Downs steward, and at the time of his interview for this book, he was the Blue Ribbon Downs clerk of scales. Harley has three children: Tommy Ray, Harley Eugene, and Carolyn Sue. Harley's son, Tommy Ray, has been leading rider at Glasgow, Montana; Rock Springs, Wyoming; and Fort Pierre, South Dakota.

At the time of this interview, Harley and his wife, Ann, lived on rural acreage east of Blue Ribbon Downs near Sallisaw, in a house they designed and built. After 33 years of riding, moving from circuit to circuit, and sustaining several serious injuries, Harley decided to "semi-retire" in 1974.   From 1974–1985, Harley rode primarily at Blue Ribbon Downs for Paul Walters, a local trainer at Sallisaw.

In his role as clerk of the scales, Harley had compassion for his jockeys. He knew what it was like to struggle making weight, understood the cold mornings, hard work, and high-strung horses. Harley encouraged "his boys" through their darker moments and gave them hope. He even talked to them about putting back a portion of their winnings for retirement later. The "boys" seemed to value the advice. Maybe they realized that Harley Crosby was among the last of a great generation of Oklahoma pioneer jockeys.

William Joseph Hunt, 1934-_____

Like many of the other boys from the bushes, William "Willie" Hunt's young life evolved around horses. His dad farmed and raised horses around Jenks, Oklahoma. Along with horses and crops, Willie's parents, Bill and Lydia Hunt, raised nine kids on their Oklahoma farm. Little Willie was small for his age, and at 10 years old and 45 pounds, he was a natural rider.

Willie loved to run his horse, Brownie, against anyone who would race him. Soon, Bill Hunt became aware of his son's ability and one day tossed Willie up on one of his racing mares during a match race on a straightaway bush track near home. Willie won easily and suddenly was swept up into his dad's world of horse racing.

Willie Hunt at Newkirk, 1954 winning on Mackett owned by O.E. "Hug" Davis.

Riding for his dad and later his stepfather, William Crenshaw, Willie spent his childhood in a saddle. Before he even knew what was happening, he had become a jockey. He rode at Newkirk, Enid, Pond Creek, Pawhuska, Tulsa, and Wagoner in Oklahoma, and Burden and Anthony in Kansas. He rode with all of the boys and girls from the bushes during the peak of bush track racing, and was close friends with Harley Crosby and Joe Thomas. He remembers riding against two sisters, Betty and Donna Bryant of Pryor, Oklahoma.

In the April, 1947, issue of Roundup, there is a two-frame picture with a caption that read: "Little Joe noses out Leo in 250-yard match race, March 8 at Tulsa. At right: Little Billy Hunt bats Baldy to win by neck over Goodeye for 350-yard match at Tulsa." In 1948 at the Pawhuska track, Willie won on Little Joe against Bourbon. He had ridden both horses before and was not that surprised when Little Joe day lighted Bourbon. Willie won his first $100 at that race, a small fortune to him.

Willie rode a match race in Sallisaw one bright day. His horse won, but ran off with him. He was much too small to get control of the horse, so he hung on for dear life as the horse jumped ditches and ran a good quarter of a mile before he finally tired and stopped.

On another day when Willie first began riding, his dad set up a match race with one of his horses against Gomer Evan's race car. The match race took place on a dirt track near Tulsa. Willie won on Stony Joe, a Painted Joe colt, because the car spun out on the dirt track. By the time the tires caught hold, Willie and Stony Joe were long gone.

Some of the great horses Willie rode along the way included Spotted Spider, Black Label, Half Question, Paleo Pete, Vanzaretta Two, and Romo Charge. He won the first Kansas Futurity in 1952 on Paleo Pete. In 1966, he won the Kansas again on Romo Charge. In the late 1970s, he flew from Denver to Hawthorn in Chicago and won a derby on Vanzaretta Two.

Willie married former bush track rider Shirley Barnes in 1953, and the couple had three children: Jimmy, Billy, and Sue. Willie continued to ride, but worked construction jobs during the off-season to support his family.

Willie finally gave up riding in the 1970s, but continued to train horses for years. One of his fondest memories as a trainer was a mare named Miss Classy Qua. The mare belonged to J.D. Anderson and when Willie took her, they had been running her tail off. He could see she needed a rest. Willie took it easy with her, stood her in the gates, backed her down a bit, and then began to bring her back. She won her heat in the All American Sales Futurity in 1981, and two weeks later won the race, beating Easily Smashed.

Along with his many accolades as rider and trainer, Willie is proud of his children. His oldest son, Billy, won the triple crown of Quarter Horse racing in 1981 by winning the Kansas Futurity, the Rainbow Futurity, and the All American on Special Effort.

Jimmy Hunt still rides today at Sallisaw. Willie's daughter Sue trained horses at Blue Ribbon Downs in Sallisaw until it closed in 2010. Willie's youngest son, David, currently is riding in Oklahoma, Kansas, and Illinois.

Joe Fredrick Thomas, 1940-_____

Born in Bartlesville, Oklahoma, to Fred and Viva Thomas, Joe Thomas had his own horse when he was 5 years old. Fred Thomas paid $6 for Tar Baby at an auction, and the pony almost tore the horse trailer up on the way home. Although Joe's first horse was a handful, he soon had Tar Baby under control and the two grew up racing down country roads and exploring the nearby Oklahoma hills.

Joe Thomas won on Caliga in 1956 at Burden, Kansas.

Joe learned to rope from his dad, and at an early age was roping, riding bareback, and climbing on bulls at the local rodeos. By age 9, he began to ride in match races near his home. Later, he lived and rode near Pawhuska and Ponca City.

In 1952, at age 12, Joe won his first official race on the track at Newkirk, riding Painted Joe Jr. He ended up riding Painted Joe Jr. 27 times, winning 26 times and pulling him once. Joe also rode Dynamo Leo for Tom Searcy.

He credits Dee Garrett, who trained Vandy's Flash, for helping him in those early days to develop his riding skills.

Joe rode the bush tracks in Newkirk, Enid, Pawhuska, and Fairfax in Oklahoma, and in Burden and Howard, Kansas. During his career as a jockey, he also rode in Detroit, Suffolk Downs in New Hampshire, Massachusetts, Rhode Island, Washington Park in Chicago, and in Denver. He rode with or knew nearly every rider, including Eldon Nelson, who he met at Washington Park in Chicago. Joe rode with Clayton and Kenny Epperson, and later rode Bobby Bud for Paul Epperson. Many of the bush track riders rode with Joe in the bushes, and later rode for him.

At age 32, Joe stopped riding and quickly transitioned into training horses for the track. He trained horses for Albert Hogoboom for more than 30 years in Eldorado, Kansas. Some of the outstanding horses Joe had the privilege of handling were Showgun, Jumbo Pacific, The Chronicle, and Turnpoint.

Today, Joe lives with his wife, Betty, near Eureka, Kansas, where he continues to train horses. He has four children—Brenda, Shawn, Jim, and Joe.

In 2010, at the summer meet in Eureka, Kansas, fellow bush track riders Clayton Epperson and Herman Moore visited with Joe and watched his horses run. Floyd Campbell came from Arizona to ride Joe's horses during the meet. The four old riders reminisced about the way things were "back in the day."

Johnny Grizzard, 1941-_____

Johnny Grizzard was born in LaGrange, Georgia, but moved to Oklahoma and went to work for Bill Beshears at the fairgrounds in Claremore when he was 17. At the age of 8, Johnny and the neighbor kids had match raced their ponies down the dirt roads near his dad's Georgia farm. He became hooked on the thrill of racing at an early age.

Vernie Willis from Claremore helped Johnny a lot in his early career as a jockey. Johnny was a hard worker and determined to become a good rider, so he eventually found his way from the bush tracks at Newkirk, Vinita, Woodward, Miami, and Ponca City to Ruidoso and Raton.

Through the years of riding in the bushes, Johnny rode with Charlie Burr, Rabbit Wells, Floyd Campbell, Herman Moore, Jackie Myers, Tecumseh Starks, Harley Crosby, Otis Craighead, Roy Brooks, Joe Thomas, and Willie Hunt.

Fellow rider Harley Crosby witnessed the accident at Blue Ribbon Downs in 1992 that forever changed Johnny's life. Harley was in the grandstand watching colts run a schooling race, when Johnny's horse jumped the rail, leaped up into the stands, and fell on him. The doctors gave Johnny no chance to survive, but they did not understand the courage and tenacity of an old bush track rider.

Johnny's days in the irons ended in 1992, and he continues to battle the odds against mounting health problems, but he keeps in contact with several of his fellow bush track riders and remains an avid race fan.

Some of the great horses Johnny rode in his day were Streaky Bars, Bayou Bars, Chemelita, and Dixie Dial.

Calvin Stone, 1932–2010

Born in Davenport, Oklahoma, Calvin Stone grew up near the rural farm town of Fairfax. At an early age, he began to ride and then break horses for neighbors around his dad's farm. In 1946, at age 14, he rode his first match race on Flicka at a bullring track in Cushing, Oklahoma.

Like some of the other bush track riders, Calvin does not remember if he won that first race, but he remembers that the thrill of the ride put horse racing in his blood forever. Shortly after that match race, men around Fairfax and Ralston began to come pick Calvin up every weekend and take him with them to tracks around Oklahoma and Kansas to ride their horses.

In those early years, Calvin broke and rode horses for George Braden, who lived between Fairfax and Ponca City. He learned a lot about horses and racing from George, and they remained friends throughout the years.

Calvin won his first purse race at Burden, Kansas. The track would put up money, owners would pay an entry fee, and a dollar would be collected from spectators to help make up the purse. Calvin's most memorable races during his bush track days were Miss Pawhuska over Bob KK at Enid, Blackman Burdick over Little Peppy at Pond Creek, and Gold King Bailey losing to Bob KK at Pawhuska.

When Calvin lost the race against Bob KK, the owner was upset and blamed Calvin. A week later, another match race took place between the same two horses, with a different rider on Gold King Bailey. Bob KK won again. Later on, Calvin rode Miss

Pawhuska, the Quarter Horse mare of the year in 1949, owned by Dee Garrett, and won over Bob KK.

Calvin joined the Marine Corps in 1951 and did not ride much upon his return, but he still had a few memorable experiences on the bush tracks as late as 1962, just before the Newkirk track closed forever.

Calvin Stone in Enid on Blackman owned by Russel Burdick.

In a serendipitous way, Calvin Stone played a part in planting the seed for this book. Clayton Epperson invited author Lou Dean to go with him to Remington Park in Oklahoma City to watch the horse races on August 18, 2007. While at Remington, Calvin's Thoroughbred, Here Comes Marv, with Boyd Caster as the trainer and Martin Escobar riding, won a seven-furlong race.

Clayton and his friend Jim Walker let out a whoop when Here Comes Marv won, and said, "Come on, let's go get in the win picture."

"Do you know this owner?" Lou Dean asked. "Will it be okay with him?"

"Known him for 60 years," Clayton replied. "We rode in the bushes together."

"What are the bushes?" Lou asked, walking fast to make it to the win circle. It was the question that led to the beginning of this book.

Two horses won two separate races at Newkirk one Sunday. In typical "bush track fashion" the two owners began to brag, "My horse is better." A match race was scheduled for mid-week, and Calvin, who then worked at the meat-packing plant in Arkansas City, Kansas, was asked to ride BuckCheshawalla, a horse being trained by Don Hartley. The other horse, owned by George Banan and trained by Joe Thomas, would be ridden by Joe Thomas. The race was for 300 yards and each owner put up $300 cash. Calvin showed up at the track after work late that afternoon to find a group of interested bystanders gathered.

"BuckCheshawalla outran the other horse by a head," Calvin recalled. "Joe Thomas and George Banan were so disappointed they couldn't even curse. I left the track and went and bought them a case of beer, set it under a tree for them, and left."

Calvin Stone rode on the following bush tracks between 1946–1950: Newkirk, Miami, Pawhuska, Enid, Cushing, Pond Creek, and Woodward in Oklahoma, and Anthony, Liberal, Burden, Howard, and Eureka in Kansas.

At the time of his interview, Calvin lived with his wife, Wanda, in Newkirk, Oklahoma. He owned and raced a string of fine Thoroughbred horses at Remington, Will Rogers, and Blue Ribbon Downs in Oklahoma, and at Oaklawn Park in Arkansas.

Sometimes he would drive by the old Newkirk race track and recall the glory days. He said he could still picture some of the owners' names that used to be above the stalls: Allie Wilson, Orie Meeks, A.G. Pappan, Lynn Payne, who owned Kay County Bill and Rock n Roll, John Speck, and Red Connely. He remembered the renovation of the Newkirk Race Track in 1947, when they built the barns and redid the track. The track had been used for sulky races in earlier years.

Calvin knew many of the riders. He rode against Clayton Epperson, Joe Thomas, Rabbit Wells, Herman Moore, Janet Barnes, Willie Hunt, and Wantha Davis. Calvin remembered riding against Wantha, the first woman rider, twice at the Newkirk racetrack.

"Wantha rode a horse named Blob Jr," Calvin said.

Two of Calvin's step-brothers, Jackie and Herschel Radford, followed in his footsteps to become boys from the bushes. Herschel rode the bush tracks for years and became leading rider in 1947 at Ruidoso, New Mexico. Jackie rode mostly at Grand Island, Omaha and Lincoln, Nebraska, and was leading bug boy there his first year.

Wantha Lorena Bangs Davis, 1917-2012

Wantha Davis grew up on the outskirts of Liberal, Kansas, riding her pony, Merrylegs, around the rural community. By age 7, she fancied herself a trick rider and spent endless hours standing, jumping, and hanging on Merrylegs, who would, in self-defense, occasionally scrape Wantha off on a low-hanging limb.

Wantha always had at least one dog for an audience. Her canine friends would obediently line up and watch their master perform, applauding with enthusiastic wags of their bushy tails. Her favorite dog, Pupsy, a half-coyote/Shepherd remained her constant companion throughout childhood.

Wantha Bangs Davis wins a match race in Texas in 1936

Wantha Bangs Davis standing, far left, in front of wooden starting gates used in late '30s and early '40s.

Twelve-year-old Wantha was so immersed in horses that she barely noticed the Depression and Dust Bowl difficulties following the crash of the New York Stock Exchange in 1929. By then she had, however, taken notice of the horse races at the Liberal Fair near her home, and had begun to ride her new horse, Goldie, to the track every chance she got. Wantha soon had an urge to do more than watch.

Wantha knew she could ride as good as any of the boys in the neighborhood. She began to envision herself on the back of a fast horse blasting down that racetrack. At 15, opportunity knocked when a neighbor allowed her to ride a black mare named Baby Jo in the horse race at Liberal, Kansas.

With no gates, the "lap and tap" race was the beginning of a colorful career for young Wantha. Her reputation as a good rider slowly spread. Soon, other neighbors began asking her to break their horses and train them to run. Within a year, she was traveling to local fairs and racetracks, exercising and riding racehorses.

This progression from playing trick rider on Merrylegs to becoming a jockey came

Wantha in the win circle at Riverside Park in McLoud, Oklahoma.

natural to Wantha. She loved horses and had an adventurous spirit that led her quickly into the bigger arena of horse racing.

Wantha's mother played a big part in her daughter's later success. Although Emma Bangs may have secretly worried about young Wantha's budding jockey career, she allowed her daughter to compete in the male-dominated sport. Emma had lost her own mother at age 5, and was raised for the most part by her father. She grew up independent and encouraged Wantha to do the same.

The summer before she graduated from high school, Wantha stepped up on a Rock Island freight train bound for a race meet she had heard about in Amarillo, Texas. She does not remember if she bought a ticket, just that the conductors were very nice and let her ride in the caboose, where it was more comfortable. The train stopped often to load cattle into the freight cars while Wantha watched with interest. She had about 50 cents in her jeans and no idea what was ahead.

She arrived in Amarillo, found the racetrack, and immediately got a job exercising horses in the early mornings before the races. Each day, she used three cents out of her quarter earnings to send a letter home to her mother. The adventure lasted only a few weeks, but when Wantha returned to Kansas, she was more determined than ever to be a rider.

After she graduated from Liberal High School, Wantha broadened her competitions, riding in Dodge City, Winfield, and Hartnew, Kansas, and Seiling, Oklahoma. She met Mrs. Mathis at a Kansas meet, and the two became instant companions. Mrs. Mathis had a fast mare named Jesse Dean and needed a dependable rider, so Wantha agreed to travel the fair circuit that summer and ride Jesse Dean. That relationship went on into the winter, and Mrs. Mathis, her son, his wife, and Wantha spent several months racing in Phoenix, Arizona, and Bakersfield, California. In the spring, they returned to the Mathis place outside of Seiling, Oklahoma, and began to prepare horses for the summer meets in Oklahoma and neighboring states.

While riding for Mrs. Mathis, Wantha met her future husband, Lendol Davis. Lendol asked Wantha to travel with him to Oklahoma and ride a horse in a race at Chickasha. Lendol took Wantha to the Davis ranch near Duncan, Oklahoma, where Wantha stayed briefly with Lendol's mother and later with his sister while she rode his horses at the weekend meet.

For the next three years, Wantha traveled the racing circuits, exercising and riding horses for Mrs. Mathis, Davis, and other owners. She traveled across Kansas, Oklahoma, New Mexico, and California riding regular scheduled races and match races. Anyone who hired Wantha to ride soon found out she was hard working and dependable, so they always would hire her back.

Wantha married Lendol in 1939 at a Baptist Church in Albuquerque, New Mexico, after she rode at a weekend race meet in Albuquerque. Wantha said, "He may have been interested in me from the beginning. I don't know. I was more interested in horses back then."

Before they married, Lendol had purchased the mare Jesse Dean from Mrs.

Mathis. When they married, Lendol surprised Wantha with the news, and Wantha later won the New Mexico Handicap at the New Mexico State Fair on the mare. Wantha and Lendol raised and successfully ran several of Jesse Dean's foals.

In 1941, Wantha rode relay races during Frontier Days in Cheyenne, Wyoming, and then traveled to Washington State where she galloped horses. In 1942 and 1943, she galloped horses at Churchill Downs and Douglas Park in Louisville, Kentucky, and in Ohio. She also galloped at River Downs in Columbus, Beulah Park, and Ascot Park at Akron, and Randal Park in Cleveland, Ohio.

By 1943, Wantha became the first female rider in U.S. Jockey Club history to run in state-sanctioned pari-mutuel races. She rode in Lincoln, Hastings, and Columbus, Nebraska, for nationally recognized trainers including racing hall of fame trainer Marion Van Berg. She was one of the leading jockeys alongside hall of fame rider Basil James and the top U.S. jockey of 1936, Ralph Neves.

When Lendol was drafted into the Army in 1944 and spent nine months in Italy, Wantha did not let her husband's absence, nor the fact that she was a mother, interfere with her riding. She enlisted the help of her sister to assist in the care of her young son, Tad, loaded up the house trailer, and proceeded to the East Coast race circuit. Tad changed schools five times in the first grade.

For the next two years, Wantha remained in Redlands, California, where Tad could stay in the same school. She galloped horses at Santa Anita and rode match races in the state. When the war ended in 1945, Lendol returned and the couple once again hit the racing circuits.

In 1946 and 1947, Wantha rode the bush tracks in Kansas, Texas, and Oklahoma, competing anywhere there was a horse race. Living mostly in their house trailer, Wantha, Lendol, Tad, and several dogs led a life on the road.

In 1949, at a special exhibition race in Agua Caliente, Mexico, Wantha beat racing hall of fame jockey Johnny Longden. Thousands of spectators crossed the border from San Diego to watch Wantha outrace Longden by a length and three-quarters in the six furlong match race. The three-time national champion was so mad that he yanked off his tack and refused to weigh out.

Wantha later defeated hall of famer Glen Lasswell at the same track, as well as hall of fame rider Basil James in Nebraska.

Wantha raced two seasons in Tucson, Arizona, in the late 1940s, riding both Thoroughbreds and Quarter Horses. She won the Arizona Derby on her own horse, Little Robert. She also rode in Las Vegas, Nevada; Vessels Ranch, California; and numerous other tracks in California.

In her career, Wantha rode for Walter Merrick as well as for Rex C. Ellsworth, breeder and trainer of 1955 Kentucky Derby winner Swaps.

At age 34, Wantha competed in special exhibition races at Exhibition Park in Vancouver, Canada, and at Pimlico in Baltimore, Maryland, where she made the national newsreel. For the next five years, until she was 40 years old, Wantha continued to race in Oklahoma and Kansas.

From 1957 through 1978, Wantha and Lendol worked the family ranch near Duncan, Oklahoma, breaking and training colts for the racetrack. Wantha finally traded in her jockey saddle for a stock saddle and retired from racing, but she remained on a horse until she was 78 years old. After her husband of 39 years passed away in 1978, Wantha continued to run the 850-acre family ranch in Oklahoma.

Twelve years after Wantha Bangs Davis retired, a woman jockey, Kathy Kushner, finally successfully sued for a license under the Civil Rights Act.

Wantha Davis is a living pioneer of horse racing. Throughout her career, she demonstrated the true spirit of the American West. The fact that she never had a dressing room, never received a license to ride on a nationally sanctioned pari-mutuel track, yet always kept a good attitude in order to compete, speaks well of her character and tenacity.

Although it's difficult for Wantha to remember which Oklahoma bush tracks she rode and the riders she competed against, many of the older jockeys remember her. She was well known and liked. All of the other girl riders from the bush track days say Wantha opened the door for them. More than one of the girl riders from the bushes said, "When things got tough and I was scared, I'd think, Wantha Davis outrode Johnny Longden." The boys from the Oklahoma bushes who remember Wantha say "she was a tough little rider."

In 2004, Wantha Lorena Bangs Davis was inducted into the National Cowgirl Museum Hall of Fame in Fort Worth, Texas.

Barbara Ann Berry Chase, 1933-2010

Barbara Ann Berry was born in Konawa, Oklahoma, where her young life revolved around horses. By the time she was 2 years old, Barbara already had a dream to become a trick rider. Her earliest memory is being sick in bed and persuading her brother, Gene, to bring her Shetland, Tony, into the house when their parents were gone one afternoon. Her brother then held Tony while Barbara jumped from the bed to the pony, practicing her tricks. Unfortunately, on the way out the door Tony took a bite out of a pumpkin that lay inside the front porch, so the two got caught.

Barbara got at least half of her tenacity from her mother, Allie Lee Minton Berry, born in Indian Territory in 1896. According to family history, Grandfather Minton decided to go to Arizona in a covered wagon in 1906. Barbara's mother, Allie, then 10 years old, had to walk and lead the milk cow the entire distance. When they arrived in Arizona, Grandfather Minton decided, after two nights, that he did not like the state so they loaded up and returned to Konawa. Allie led the milk cow all the way back to Oklahoma.

A fond early memory for Barbara is sitting with her father, Luther A. Berry, behind their barn one day and listening to him talk about his dream: "I'm going to take that broodmare, Sunny Lynn, and breed her to a stud that Allen Whitworth has, and we will get a colt that will be able to compete with the best. Maybe we will make it to the Kentucky Derby one day." With a spark in his eyes, Luther looked down at his daughter and added, "You can be my jockey."

Barbara, of course, had no idea that girls could not ride on official tracks back in those days, so her father's dream became her new dream. She spent endless hours riding a horse named Old Bird in pretend races. Old Bird was her father's match race mare out of E.W. Marland stock.

At age 8, Barbara's daydreams turned to reality when an opportunity to ride in a real race presented itself one day at a county fair in Duncan, Oklahoma. A Shetland pony race for kids 10 and under was in progress when Barbara and her father arrived at the fairgrounds. Luther quickly noticed that a man was having trouble with his little girl and her Shetland. The Shetland kept turning around and fighting to go back to the barn, and the girl could not handle him.

Luther spoke up, "My little girl can get that horse on the track if you'd like her to ride him."

Before Barbara even knew what was happening, her father gave her a leg up onto the Shetland and instructed her: "Take this whip and spank his butt a couple of times. Let him know who is boss. When they give the signal to start, ride like there's a prairie fire behind you."

Barbara won her first race that day. Not only was she a jockey, she was a rich jockey. The man paid her $5. She never had held that much money in her hand. It was the beginning, and Luther quickly enlisted Barbara to ride his horses.

Luther had a little Quarter Horse mare named Nancy Berry who he immediately put Barbara on. Nancy Berry was extremely fast out of the gate and tough to beat for 200 yards. She would squat in the gate and fire like a rocket, so Barbara learned a lot from little "Nancy." Another early horse Barbara learned on was a Thoroughbred mare named Fashion Girl who Luther owned.

In 1942, the Oklahoma/Kansas Thoroughbred Racing Association was formed, and the first race meet was held in Clinton, Oklahoma. The meet continued in Kingfisher, Pond Creek, Seiling, Fairview, Tolga, and Woodward, then went to Kansas in Eureka, Anthony, and Wichita.

One horse Barbara remembers distinctly was named Loch Moeve. A man named Charlie Mitchell was running the big black horse in Oklahoma, but the horse's papers

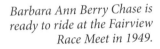

Barbara Ann Berry Chase is ready to ride at the Fairview Race Meet in 1949.

Barbara Ann Berry Chase won on Glider Girl, owned and trained by her father, Luther Berry with brother, Roscoe holding horse, Barbara's mom, sister, far right, and nephew Ricky on the horse with Barbara.

were not recognized by the New York Jockey Club. This was during World War II and the United States Army had liberated Loch Moeve and other horses from Hitler's stables. Although the horses were papered in the German Jockey Club, those credentials were not accepted in the United States.

Another horse Barbara remembers was Josephine R, owned by Simon Scott of Duncan, Oklahoma. The mare was a witch in the starting gate, but could outrun anything she ever ran against from 300 yards up to three-eighths of a mile. Barbara also rode the mother of Painted Jo Jr., who became a famous match race horse.

Early in Barbara's jockey career, she had the opportunity to go to Albuquerque, New Mexico, and compete against Wantha Davis. Wantha was the only girl jockey Barbara knew of at that time. Barbara and her father started to New Mexico, but a huge flood stopped them. Barbara was extremely disappointed when she learned the following year that girls could no longer ride in the Albuquerque meet.

Barbara rode Stonewall Dick, owned by Audie Murphy's widow, not the movie star, in the first Oklahoma Futurity finals in Tulsa in 1947. The inside rail on the track was a string on little stakes. She drew the inside position and the minute she left the gate a horse owned by Bud Warren named Flit took to the left and squeezed her off of the track into the infield. Flit was disqualified for bumping. Warren also owned Lota W, who was in the number 6 spot that day and was credited with winning the race.

Barbara walked into win circles from 1942 until the early '50s. From Riverside Park in McLoud, Oklahoma, to Woodward and Kingfisher, and to Liberal and Anthony, Kansas, the young jockey pursued her dream. She won on Miss Billie Van, owned by Burl Surber. By 1945, she won on the first horse she ever owned, Fashion Girl, in King-fisher. She took first on Dream Beauty, owned by F. Winklepek, in Liberal in 1950; Miss Headache, owned by Ike Ritter, in Anthony, Kansas; and on Johnny Mack, owned by J. O. Allen, in Liberal, Kansas, in 1950. She also rode at Pawhuska, Enid, and Pond Creek. Barbara rode Hank H. in Tulsa, in the last race he ever ran.

In 1945, at a race in Pawhuska, Barbara was asked to ride a Thoroughbred named Lot A Gold. By then, Barbara was pretty cocky about her riding ability. The owner told Barbara not to try to rate the horse, to let her break and set her own pace.

Barbara says she had daylight around the first turn, and then another horse came up on her and stayed right by her around the stretch, and then managed to beat her. Barbara took second and sensed that the owner was really disappointed in her. A couple of weeks later she overheard that the jockey who beat her, Billy Mitchell, had bragged to the guys that he had held onto her saddle pad and made Barbara's horse pull him most of the way. After that, Barbara became more aggressive.

At a race in Seiling, Oklahoma, one weekend, she was riding a Thoroughbred in a 4½-furlong race. On the first turn, a jockey came up on the inside, reached for her foot, and tried to flip her out of the saddle. Barbara hit him several times with her bat and busted his goggles. After the race, the announcer said, "Barbara Berry, report to the judges stand." Barbara was scared as she walked toward the judges.

"Did you hit that jockey in the face with your bat?" a judge asked.

"Yes, I did," Barbara admitted. "He grabbed my foot and tried to flip me out of my saddle."

The judges ran the other rider off and told him not to come back.

Another time, a Mexican rider came up beside her in a race, put his hand on her hand, and said, "Take hold of him, Beautiful."

Barbara whopped him with her bat and won the race.

A classic picture taken around 1946 shows 11 raggedy boys and two girl jockeys sitting and kneeling on the bush track railing at Pond Creek. Their ages appear to range from 8 years to young adult. Next to Barbara Berry Chase sits Joyce Riggs Church. A few of the other riders identified are Charlie Murrah, Clyde Waller, and "Jake" Jacobs.

Barbara competed often with Joyce Riggs, and considered her a friend and a tough competitor. She also rode against Wantha Davis on several occasions, and knew Charlie Burr.

Barbara met her husband, Richard T. Chase, in 1951. She had taken a job as a car hop at a drive-in to make money to buy a car. Richard came in every evening after work to drink a beer and visit. Earlier that summer, he'd been in the grandstands in Ada, Oklahoma, and seen Barbara ride. Although Richard was not a horseman, he loved horses. The two were married in November, 1951. Barbara gave up her jockey career to become a wife, but continued to help her father raise and train horses.

Luther Berry produced many fine racing Quarter Horses, including a stallion named Allie Be First, who competed in Sallisaw in the futurity trials in 1970. Allie Be First had shin-bucked and still ran second in his heat. In those same futurity trials, a little-known horse named Easy Jet also competed.

At the time of this interview, Barbara owned and managed an 86-acre ranch in Konawa. She lost her husband of 58 years in March of 2009. Barbara, at 76, still continues to pursue the dream her father shared—of raising an outstanding running Quarter Horse. She had two hopefuls on the track during the 2010 season.

"I don't know how many horses I have," said Barbara. "I learned long ago not to take an inventory of your horses, 'cause all you are going to hear is 'That's too many.' Walter Merrick told me that, and he proved it when he raised Easy Jet."

Floyd McKinley Campbell, 1951-_____

Born and raised in Ponca City, Oklahoma, Floyd Campbell was another prominent black rider who began his career in the bushes. His parents, Floyd and Aletha, often sent their young son to spend the summers on Grandmother McCellen's farm near Henryetta, Oklahoma.

Floyd was drawn toward horses at an early age, but his grandmother said he could not ride. He would sneak out to the barn when Grandma was busy and get up on the horses without a saddle or bridle. Just sitting on a horse, feeling the movement beneath him, filled Floyd with an excitement that would lead him toward a lifetime career.

Jackie Myers and Tecumseh Starks had paved the way for a black boy to become a respected rider on the Oklahoma bush tracks in the early 1950s. Herman Moore, 10 years Floyd's senior, also had opened doors that made it easier for Floyd. Older bush track riders like Clayton Epperson, who by the late '60s had become a trainer, gave Floyd early chances to ride. Joe Thomas, Bob Johnson, Frank R. Thompson, Don Farris, Leo Wood, and J.B. Montgomery also helped Floyd along the way. Walter Merrick influenced Floyd and opened doors of opportunity for him by giving him the chance to ride some nice horses.

Floyd rode the Oklahoma tracks in Newkirk, Sallisaw, Claremore, Kiefer, Woodward, Laverne, and Miami. He rode in Hutchinson and Wichita, Kansas, and in Joplin, Missouri.

His very first race in the bushes was memorable because he had no jockey boots. He put on two pair of thick socks, which proved to be painful when he had to stand up in the stirrups to stop the horse at the end of the race.

The greatest horse Floyd remembers from his early career was a Quarter Horse named, Shakey Embrujo. Floyd won the Kansas Jackpot, the American Air Lines Challenge, and numerous other races on Shakey Embrujo.

Floyd rode with or for most of the early bush track riders and was well liked and respected by all who knew him. His personality and experience allowed him to move easily from rider to steward in early 2005. Floyd's impressive list of credentials include: Steward—Prescott, Arizona, 2005–2006; Steward—Arizona County Fairs, 2004–2006; Steward—North Dakota, 2006–2007; Steward—Evanston, Wyoming, 2006–2007; Paddock Judge—Turf Paradise, 2007–2010; Claims Clerk—Turf Paradise, 2006–2010; Clocker—Turf Paradise, 2006–2007; Race Office Lasix—Turf Paradise, 2008; and Jockey, 37 years.

In 1997, Floyd stepped into the world of film when he joined the cast of Buffalo Soldiers, a made-for-television movie staring Danny Glover. Floyd was able to put his rid-

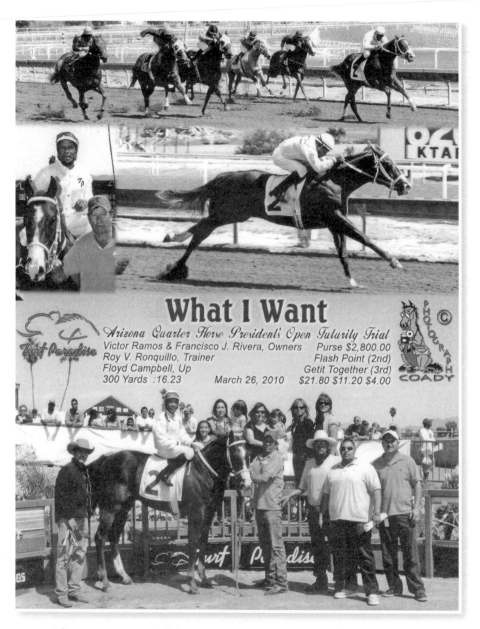

After Many years out of the irons, Floyd got an urge to ride in 2009 at age 57. On March 26, 2010, he won the Arizona Quarter Horse President's Open Futurity on What I Want. Three weeks later he rode the same horse to victory in the Futurity.

Floyd Campbell wins in 1969 at the Ponca Turf Club Riding Scottso, owned and trained by Clayton Epperson. Clayton, at the back in the straw hat, his wife Phyllis, front in the sheepskin coat, Kenny Epperson to her right, and the next generation of Eppersons.

ing experience in the bushes to good use. Floyd was one of 30 picked from a pool of 400. "They were looking for Afro-Americans who could ride horses," Floyd told the *Ponca City News*.

"I rode and they picked me right on the spot," Floyd told the *Trinidad Chronicle News*.

A picture of Floyd with Danny Glover appeared in the *Ponca City News* on June 11, 1997. In cavalry uniform, standing 5' 2", Floyd barely comes to Glover's shoulder.

In 2009, at age 57, Floyd got an irrepressible urge to return to the saddle. On February 2, 2009, he got a standing ovation when the announcer told the audience it was Floyd's first win after his recent return to the irons.

On March 26, 2010, Floyd won the Arizona Quarter Horse President's Open Futurity Trial on a horse named What I Want. Three weeks later, Floyd won that Futurity on What I Want.

On April 27, 2010, Floyd rode Jesstifiable to victory in the El Moro de Cumpas stakes race at the Santa Cruz County Fairgrounds in Sonoita, Arizona. Floyd won on Jesstifiable previously in Douglas and Tucson, Arizona, breaking three track records along the way.

With poise and humility, the old Oklahoma bush track rider said to the press, "This is just a nice horse. I'm fortunate enough to be able to ride him."

Then Floyd added, "I won't be retiring any time soon."

Roy Dean Brooks, 1941-_____

Although Roy Brooks grew up on a ranch near Blanchard, Oklahoma, he did not ride horses much during his childhood. On a couple of occasions, he rode briefly with his cousins, Jack and Monty Brooks, but horses did not interest him back then. In the early 1960s, however, he began to exercise horses for his brother, Ron. Even though Roy liked the thrill of horse racing, he had little confidence and never dreamed of becoming a jockey.

Roy's dad, Dub, bought a couple of horses that were out of the sire Good Bird and began to run them on the local circuit. In 1964, a neighbor, W.W. Wilson, won the All American with champion Decketta. Roy's interest in racing began to grow.

Roy Brooks' jockey career began by accident in 1966. Roy had gone in partners with his father on a palomino mare named Star Lady Bruce. When Roy became frustrated with the way the mare was being ridden, he decided he could do a better job than the jockeys. At Greer Downs in Mangum, Oklahoma, 24-year-old Roy climbed aboard Star Lady Bruce. He was so terrified in the gate that he could not even manage to spit.

Roy Dean Brooks, in his first race, rode Star Lady Bruce to victory in Mangum, Oklahoma. Roy's dad, left, with brothers, left and right, with wife Connie and kids Becky and Jimmy.

Coming out of the gate, he lost both stirrups but somehow hung on and won the race.

At that time, Roy never imagined he would end up riding for the next 40 years, but the thrill of riding first across that finish line did not go away. In 1966, Roy was married with children and working a full-time night job as a frame wireman for Bell Telephone Company. Even though he began to toy with the idea of riding full time, quitting the security of his job was not that easy.

Roy began exercising racehorses during the day for his uncle Jack Byers. By then, his cousin Jack Brooks had a stable just down the road and was beginning his legend-

Roy Brooks Rides 5 Winners on Sunday's Remington Park Card

Roy Brooks, the dean of the Remington Park jockey colony at age 67 and the oldest jockey still competing in North American horse racing, won five races on the Sunday night card. The quintuple blasted him into second-place in the rider standings.

Brooks, a rancher from Blanchard, Okla. in his non-racing time, put together his best night of the season on Sunday night. The big evening of winning started in the third race with CJS Friend ($17.80 to win). He won three consecutive races from the fifth thru the seventh with Stolis Royal ($5), Docs Dusty Okie ($11.20) and Eyes Jess Racin ($9.40). The fifth triumph came with Justa La Jolla ($6) in the ninth race.

The five wins for Brooks ties his personal best at Remington Park for wins in one racing program. He previously had won five races on the same card two other times in his career.

The Brooks family had a hand in six of the 11 wins on Sunday. Jimmy Brooks, Roy's son, rode A Royal Cartel ($31.60) to victory in race four.

The 2009 American Quarter Horse & Mixed Breed Season moves to a Thursday thru Sunday schedule beginning this week on

March 19. Regular post time every night is 6:25 p.m.

Next weekend's feature event is the Grade 3, $355,000 Oklahoma

Futurity on Saturday night. The Oklahoma Futurity is the longest consecutively run futurity in Quarter Horse racing.

ROY BROOKS

An article and photo of Roy Brooks published 2009...still riding at 67.

ary training career. Roy rode at Wild Horse Downs, at Ratliff City, south of Lindsey, and at Red River Downs. He rode an Indian race at Anadarko with no saddle.

On weekends, Roy traveled the bush track circuits when he could. On a trip to the track in Anthony, Kansas, he and his wife, Connie, took their kids with the intention of camping in a tent. Tornados threatened Kansas that weekend, however, and it was impossible to get the tent up because of high winds. The Brooks family ended up sleeping in the car. The dust was so bad that the riders could not even see each other on the track. It was the last trip Roy ever took to Anthony Downs.

Roy rode with Charlie Smith, Harley Crosby, Willie Hunt, and G.R. Carter. Roy gives credit to Bud Morris and Jack Brooks for helping him in those early days. He fondly remembers fellow bush track rider Crosby, when Harley later became clerk of scales at Blue Ribbon Downs.

"No one could cheat Harley on weight, because he knew all of the tricks," Roy said.

In 1971, Roy gave up his job and went to ride full time for Jack Brooks at La Mesa Park. His record during those early years is a testament to his tenacity. He won a couple of races in 1968, but got fired by his brother, Ron. He won the Oklahoma Derby on Jet Space and then got fired again. Jimmy Jones fired Roy after he ran second in the Oklahoma Futurity for riding his horse too hard. Roy later agreed with that decision and always learned from his mistakes, regrouped, and returned to the track.

From 1971 to 1987, Roy lived with his family in Blanchard, Oklahoma, but would take them to La Mesa Park in Raton, New Mexico, and Ruidoso Downs in Ruidoso, for the summer. Sometimes they had a good income, sometimes they struggled, but Roy never regretted his decision to become a jockey.

Since jockey records began being kept in 1972, Roy rode 1,562 winners and his mounts earned more than $14.8 million. He won his first major stakes race at La Mesa Park in the Oklahoma Derby on Jet Space in 1972. His second major stakes race, also in 1972, was on Fly Laico Bird in the $70,198 Columbus Triple Crown Futurity at Columbus, Texas. In 1987, Roy won on Oh Bid Go in the $197,286 Colorado Stallion Breeders' Futurity at La Mesa Park. In that same year, he rode second in every major stakes at Ruidoso except the Kansas Futurity.

Roy Brooks is all-time leading rider of Paint Horses in Oklahoma. For 1993–1994 he rode 21 Paint races and had 18 wins, two seconds, and one third. He won the Pot O' Gold Futurity five times. The horses he rode include: Treasures, 1989; Texas Hero, 1993; Texas Heart, 1998; Texas Wildcat, 2001; and Cutrock, 2009.

A colorful part of Roy's history that is not shared by a lot of other riders was his passion for racing in Mexico. Roy rode match races in Mexico from 1980–2000. Mexican owners would call him, Roy would make a flight reservation, land in Guadalajara, and be driven the hour and a half to the track.

The lane on the racetrack in Mexico is divided by a string in the middle, and the race is often 100 yards. People stand everywhere on the track, and sometimes Roy would sit in the gate for as long as 30 minutes. The first time he burst out of the gate, looking at a maze of people congregated near the finish line, he just had to believe what he had been told: "They will get out of the way."

Although Roy loved the relaxed, sometimes-crazy atmosphere of the Mexican match races, the violence in Mexico had escalated so much that he finally refused to return in 2000.

On June 3, 2006, Remington Park in Oklahoma City named a race in Roy's honor, the "Roy Brooks 65th Birthday Purse." At age 65, Roy had one of his best seasons ever that spring, finishing fifth in the jockey standings at Remington Park with 31 wins.

In August 2009, Roy won a race at Blue Ribbon Downs riding a 16-year-old gelding, Silent Cash Dasher. Several articles were written about the "oldest rider winning on the oldest horse, ridden on Oklahoma's oldest racetrack."

Today, Roy is the oldest jockey still competing in North American horse racing. The oldest rider ever to win a Thoroughbred race in the United States was Frank Amonte, Sr., who won at Suffolk Downs in 2005 at age 69. Roy says he did start thinking about retirement 10 years ago, but admits it is difficult to hang up his tack when he is still winning races.

"As long as my reflexes are good and I can get good horses, I guess I'll keep riding," he said.

Roy and his wife of 51 years live on their 700-acre cattle ranch in Blanchard. Roy's high school sweetheart, Connie, has watched her husband break both ankles, his collarbone, and left fibula, but loyally remains his greatest fan. Roy and Connie have three grown children—Becky, Brenda, and Jimmy.

Jimmy, currently trying to follow in his father's stirrups, has a son, Cameron, who also is riding now. As far back as grade school, Jimmy had a dream that one day he would ride with his father. Now that dream has extended to a Family Trifecta, where Roy, Jimmy, and Cameron could ride in the same race.

Roy was inducted into the American Quarter Horse Association Hall of Fame in 2008. He was inducted into the Remington Park Racing Hall of Fame on March 3, 2010.

Roy's son, Jimmy, qualified a horse for the All American in 2010.

Lewis Brock at Hatfield's, also called Kay County Downs, in Ponca City on Cheta Gates. Jack Dye was the trainer.

Lewis Albert Brock, 1952-_____

Lewis Brock was born in Ponca City, Oklahoma, and raised near Newkirk. Most of Lewis' early memories center around horse racing. Carl Brock, Lewis' father, rode on the Oklahoma bush tracks from the early 1950s until the bush tracks closed.

61   WFTH
ilver Glove
ohnny Bob K

T-13.8

Lewis Brock's dad, Carl Brock, won at Newkirk in 1961 on Miss Space with owner Lewis Barndard, in the straw hat.

Lewis followed his father around the racetracks from the time he could toddle. At an early age, he began to walk "hots," cooling horses out by walking them after the race, for a quarter. For 50 cents, Lewis cleaned stalls.

At age 7, Lewis rode his first official race at Newkirk on the back of a Shetland pony, using a gunny sack and bailing twine for a saddle. He ran second, but the fever to become a jockey began to burn on that day in 1959.

Lewis became a serious rider at 16. He rode at Ponca City, Newkirk, Sallisaw, Stroud, Enid, and Pawhuska in Oklahoma. In later years, he rode at Louisiana Downs, Oaklawn in Arkansas, and Keystone in Pennsylvania.

At Oaklawn in 1970, Lewis rode 100 horses and lit the board 50 percent of the time. In 1980, he had the special privilege of riding against the great Willie Shoemaker at Louisiana Downs. Shoemaker was making a tour around the major tracks, riding one last race before he retired. Shoemaker won that day, and although Lewis placed fifth, it was a day he always would remember.

Lewis won the Paint Horse Futurity in 1979 at Apache Downs near Chickasha, Oklahoma, riding Charge Lady. Tommy Music was owner and trainer.

Lewis credits his dad for being his mentor, but men like George Blatchford, Jack Dye, Hug Davis, Kenny and Clayton Epperson, Nig Shultz, and John Leatherman also gave him opportunities along the way.

Lewis rode with Harley Crosby, Floyd Campbell, and Herman Moore. He rode for Joe Thomas and Calvin Stone. One of his earliest memories was of Ida Hartley, Don and Ida Hartley managed the Newkirk Race Track, nursing him back to health from rheumatic fever when he was a child. Ida came to the Brock's home in Newkirk every night for days and gave Lewis a shot to get him through the illness.

In the early 1970s, Lewis and his stepfather, Buddy Popplewell, reopened and ran the Newkirk racetrack. But with the gambling laws now strictly enforced, the era of bush track racing was fast becoming history. The new age of pari-mutuel racing was just around the corner.

From 1991–2005, Lewis broke and trained horses for his dad. Carl Brock's interest in the racetrack did not dim until his health began to diminish in 2000. As a rider, Carl won the Kansas-Bred Futurity on War Man Bars at Eureka Downs in 1963. He trained Astro Jet for George and Thelma Self of Ponca City. In his lifetime, Carl Brock trained and ran horses in Oklahoma, Texas, Louisiana, New Mexico, and West Virginia.

Between father and son, the Brock name was very familiar around the Oklahoma racing circuit.

Don Grant Allison, 1939-_____

Born to Cora Waters and Bill Allison in Prairie Grove, Arkansas, Don Allison spent his youth near Westville, Oklahoma. There, Don rode his mare, Babe, to school every day, and on weekends he raced horses with the neighbor boys. One rider, Kenneth Richards, rode match races against Don for many of those early years.

In 1949, at age 10, Don rode his first official bush track race in Wagoner, Oklahoma, on Cross Jay. Blasting out of the six-horse gate and crossing that finish line first filled Don with a passion to become a professional jockey. He loved to ride and knew he could excel.

Like many of his fellow bush track riders, Don remained in school while racing

In 1954, Don Allison rode out of his first eight-horse gate at the Oklahoma Futurity in Enid, and won on Miss Adelita.

OKLA. 2 YR. OLD FUTURITY
ENID,   OKLA.
1954

300 YARDS OKLAHOMA FUTURITY ENID, OKLA.   AUGUST 7 1954
MISS ADELITA   FIRST D. ALLISON   UP OSCAR JEFFERS JR. OWNER
BOBBIE LEO   SECOND PALLEO PETE   THIRD TIME 16.4

BREEZE BAR   JOCKEY DONALD ALLISON, UP.
THE CHICADO V. STAKE * PURSE $5000.
Winner Eighth Race   April 29, 1961.   Los Alamitos Race Course
Tonto Bars Hank (2nd)   400 yds.-:19.9   Vandy's Flash (3rd)
A NEW TRACK & WORLDS RECORD
OWNER & TRAINER: MARION SEWARD

In 1961 at Las Alamitos Race Course, Don Allison rode Breeze Bar to victory, setting a new track and world record.

on the weekends. He graduated from Westville High in 1958 and continued with his riding career.

Don rode in Wagoner, Sallisaw, Porter, Turley, Pawhuska, Newkirk, Pond Creek, Fort Gibson, Hawthorne, Gene Autry, and Enid. From 1956 through 1981, Don rode as a professional jockey in Oklahoma, New Mexico, Arizona, California, Oregon, Washington, Arkansas, and New York. He won three Oklahoma Futurities, in 1954, 1961, and 1967. He also won the Kindergarden in Los Alamitos in 1963, the Rocky Mountain Futurity in 1961, and the Los Alamitos Champions in 1977. Don rode in five All Americans and finished fourth twice.

Norris Pilgrim, Art Hines, Horace Hines, Oscar Jeffers, Jimmy Pitson, Buster Beach, and Don Tackett were some of the trainers and owners who helped Don along the way.

Don rode with Kenneth Richards, Shirley and Janet Barnes, Floyd Campbell, Herman Moore, Jackie Myers, Tecumseh Starks, Harley Eugene Crosby, Charles Cloyd Smith, Curtis William Perner, Roy Brooks, Willie Hunt, Johnny Grizzard, Joe Thomas, Wayne and Duane Murty, Bobby Ussery, and Donna Bryant. Stark and Richards were two of the riders who helped Don the most.

Some of the outstanding horses Don remembers include Miss Adelita, Miss Nellie Snip, Miss Meyers, F.L. King Bee, Bob's Folly, Midnight Charge, and Miss Tacubaya.

Don struggled constantly with his weight throughout his career. In 1981, he finally decided to hang up his tack.

Don met his wife, Linda Lee Lomax, in Skiatook in 1959. They got married in Ruidoso, New Mexico in 1961. Linda's family also was active in horse racing, so Linda and Don formed a partnership that remains active in the industry today. They currently have four Thoroughbred colts in training at their place near Collinsville, Oklahoma. Don trains at Remington Park, Will Rogers, and Fair Meadows.

Linda and Don have two sons, Donald Paul and Darren Lee.

Curtis William Perner, 1938-_____

Born in Tulsa, Oklahoma, to Edwin and Elly Perner, Curtis Perner was raised on one acre about five miles from what is now downtown Tulsa. He grew up with cows, chickens, and rabbits, but always had a fondness for horses. He had no early aspirations to become a jockey, but that changed and destiny led him down a path toward a lifetime career in horse racing.

At age 16, Curtis bought his first horse, a little Paint mare named Cherokee. One day, when Curtis happened to be riding by on Cherokee, a man named J.R. Cates asked Curtis to help him exercise a horse at a nearby ranch. Very soon, Curtis found himself working full time at Flash Farms, five miles from home. In the summer of 1954, Curtis rode Cherokee the 10-mile round trip every day to work.

The next three summers at Flash Farms, Curtis worked around the barns, learned to handle horses, and began to show the Farms' horses at the state fair.

Curtis Perner won on Johnny Do It in Bay Meadows in 1958. Hoss Inman was the owner and the trainers was B. Franklin.

In 1957, Cates wrote a letter to Walter Merrick recommending young Curtis as a potential rider. Merrick wrote back and told J.R. to send Curtis to him. Curtis began working for Merrick at 18 years of age, riding Lena's Bar, the dam of Easy Jet, out every day to feed Merrick's cattle. He would ride her across the dry riverbed, tie her to a tree limb, and feed the cows.

Curtis rode his first bush track race on Lena's Bar on a straightaway track near Weatherford, Oklahoma, in 1957. There were four horses in the race, and Lena's Bar

Curtis Perner won the All American on Tonto Bar Hands in 1960 with owners Milo and C.G. Whitcomb and trainer Pat Simpson.

ran second. He won his first race on a horse called A Car Dealer on another straight-away track off of Highway 75 between Tulsa and Okmulgee, on what they called the B Line track. He also rode a horse named Leo Bingo for Merrick, and took second at Centennial Race Track in Littleton, Colorado.

Like so many other Oklahoma boys during the bush track era, Curtis suddenly found himself unexpectedly caught up in the world of horse racing. He was a jockey. For the next 20 years, the majority of his time would be spent on the back of a fast horse.

Curtis learned by riding. During those early years, a black man named Benjamin Franklin taught him a lot about how to sit a horse and how to get ready in the gates. Franklin, who worked for Merrick, helped Curtis for two seasons.

Walter Merrick took Curtis to Centennial Race Track, where the young Oklahoma rider rode both Quarter Horses and Thoroughbreds. In that same year, 1957, Curtis went with Merrick to Albuquerque Race Track in New Mexico.

For a brief period, Curtis rode for Buffalo Wooten in Ruidoso, and later in Lubbock, Texas.

While he was riding in Colorado, Curtis met Hoss Inman. He agreed to ride for Inman that winter at his ranch in Lamar, Colorado. Inman later offered to send Curtis to San Mateo to ride horses from his stable. In 1958, Curtis won on First Call and Johnny Do It, two of Inman's horses, at Bay Meadows.

Curtis decided to strike out on his own for Ruidoso. He considered Los Alamitos, but determined there were too many seasoned riders there. Ruidoso looked like an easier place to start. When Curtis first arrived there and saw the mountains, it was love at first sight. He decided to do anything necessary to stay in the saddle near those beautiful mountains. He lived in the tack room, cleaned stalls, and galloped horses for free in the beginning.

In 1959, Curtis decided to stay in California for the night racing at Los Alamitos. Larry Machener became his agent during that time.

In 1957, Curtis rode about a dozen horses. In 1958, he was still struggling to make his way as a professional jockey. By 1959, he was on his way and by 1960 things really began to happen when he won the All American on Tonto Bars Hank in the second running of a race that would become the Quarter Horse industry's brass ring. In November 1960, Curtis again rode Tonto Bars Hank into the win circle after winning the Bardella at Los Alamitos Race Course.

In 1961, when he was on top of his game, Curtis was drafted into the Army. He came out in 1963 weighing a hefty 170 pounds. He immediately began to lose weight and started trying to get his mounts back.

In December 1964, at Los Alamitos, Curtis teamed up with trainer Bobby Mitchell and rode a 4-year-old gelding named Dari Star to victory in the Pamona Purse. From an article in Speedhorse, dated April 3, 2009, Curtis was quoted: "Dari Star had 31 starts by the time he was 4. He had 19 outs in 1963 and made $9,000. I only rode him one meeting but I remember him well. He was easy to ride and always ready to leave the gates as soon as they kicked them."

In 1965, Curtis won the first running of the Rainbow Derby on Nippy Bars. On the inside cover of the The Quarter Racing Record dated June 15, 1966, Curtis sits in the win picture on Doll Bid by Double Bid, at the Los Alamitos Race Course. The article read in part: "Making only her second start . . . Doll Bid coasted to the wire two lengths ahead of a good allowance field."

Curtis rode through all of 1964 through 1966, then the weight problem hit him again and he quit for a while. He was married, had a child, and was broke. But like most true riders, Curtis returned to the irons. Living on tuna fish and Wheat Thins to control his weight, he again proved he could ride with the best.

Throughout his career, Curtis Perner rode some great horses, including The Ole Man, More Go, Mr. Dotty Bars, and Cindy Passum. In 1978, Curtis was awarded the Jockey of the Year award from the Pacific Coast Quarter Horse Racing Association. Curtis won the New Mexico Futurity in Albuquerque in 1960 riding Bar Bright, and the New Mexico Futurity in Sunland Park in 1965 on Baby Gain.

Curtis rode with fellow Oklahoma bush track riders Herman Moore, Jackie Myers, Tecumseh Starks, and Harley Crosby in California. The group of seasoned riders helped him continue to learn more precision. He slowly developed a deep and lasting friendship with Oklahoma native Charley Smith.

"Charles Smith was my biggest help at the track," Curtis said. "He became my bud." Curtis hung up his silks in 1979, but continued to live and train horses in California at Los Alamitos for another decade. He sold his house in California and returned to Oklahoma in 1989. Today, Curtis lives on his 37-acre ranch in Wagoner, where he breeds and raises Quarter Horses. He has one daughter, Tricia, who lives in Phoenix, where she trains and shows reining horses.

Johnny L. Sellers, 1937–2010

Johnny Sellers was born on July 31, 1937, in Los Angeles, California. His parents, John H. Sellers from Claremore and Mary Pauline from Oklahoma City, settled on an acreage northeast of Tulsa when John was still a toddler.

John H. had lost his father when he was only 11 years old and had to assume the position of breadwinner for four siblings. He ran the dairy farm and later worked on highways with his team of horses and a team of mules to provide for his sisters and brothers. Johnny learned from his father that hard work was the prerequisite for success. Perhaps Johnny also inherited his love of horses from his father.

John H. bought a retired circus horse, Silver, named for the Lone Ranger's horse, for his five children to ride when Johnny was 5. Johnny would wait for Silver to lower his head, leap on the horse's neck by grabbing his mane, and scramble onto the horse's back. Silver was gentle and obliging, and often allowed many kids to ride at the same time.

Johnny rode Silver every spare moment he had in the summertime. He loved to pretend he was an Indian and decided he needed a costume. Mary Pauline was a woman of vision. She believed that her boys should learn to cook, wash, iron, clean, and do simple sewing, as well as outside chores. She agreed to teach young Johnny how to make the costume. With his mother's help, Johnny was soon proudly wearing his hand-made Indian outfit, complete with fringe.

Young Johnny loved riding so much that he would get up early in order to catch Silver and have a quick ride each morning before school. One summer day, Silver came walking home very slowly, dragging Johnny, who had one foot in the stirrup. The family later decided that Johnny had ridden too long, had sunstroke, and fainted. Silver probably saved his life. Johnny gradually developed a love and trust for horses that would lead him toward his destiny.

Twin boys named Wayne and Duane Murty happened to be in Johnny's algebra class when he attended Will Rogers High School in Tulsa. The Murty twins had been riding match races on the Oklahoma bush tracks for several years by then. In talking to Johnny, the twins could see he had a passion for the ponies. They invited him to go along with them the next weekend to one of the local bush tracks.

"Race trackers fight and curse. My mom probably won't let me go," Johnny replied.

The twins were greatly amused by his reply. They kept after young Johnny to join them. Sometime later, Johnny got permission from his parents and attended match races in Turley, Oklahoma, with the Murtys. The twins were riding for C.J. McCormick at that time, and they put Johnny up on one of McCormick's horses just to see how he rode.

Wayne and Duane were impressed with Johnny's ability. He looked like a natural, someone who had an instinct and that special ability to let a horse settle. The Murty twins encouraged Johnny, who was one year younger, to think about the possibility of becoming a professional rider. The friendship between Johnny and the Murty twins grew, and their paths crossed many times over the next 20 years.

Duane and Wayne took Johnny with them to Pawhuska one weekend, where Johnny and the twins earned 50 cents to exercise horses. Duane let Johnny take one of his mounts in a $50 match race that weekend and Johnny won. Johnny was thrilled, and by all indication made up his mind that day to become a serious rider. He immediately began to look for work around the Oklahoma bush tracks doing anything he could to get an opportunity for another race.

At 14, Johnny went to work for a prominent horse trainer, John Oxley. He cleaned stables, groomed, and cooled horses by walking them. A local dentist, Dr. Burns, and a business man, Mr. Moeller, were two of the people who met Johnny during his employment at the Oxleys. Burns and Moeller began to talk to Johnny about becoming a professional jockey, and paved the way for him to travel to Kentucky and get his early training. Burns and Moeller also persuaded Johnny's parents to sign a contract allowing their son to leave Oklahoma for Kentucky.

It must have been difficult for John and Mary Pauline to sign the papers that would send their 15-year-old boy away from home, but in the end, the Sellers were strong enough to allow their son to follow his dreams.

In the Bluegrass country of Kentucky, Johnny went to work for Harry Trotsek, trainer for Hasty House Farm. Trotsek had a good reputation for developing young riders and he encouraged Johnny. Johnny's first job was exercising the Hasty House Thoroughbreds at Churchill Downs. While in Kentucky learning to ride the fastest horses alive, Johnny attended high school, earned his GED, and took several college hours. In 1955, Johnny finished 11th at a race in Sunshine Park in one of his first professional starts. He rode 37 more horses before he got his first win. His progress for the next four years was slow, but steady.

From 1955 through 1977, Johnny worked his way in and through the world of professional horse racing. By 1961, Johnny rode Carry Back to victory in both the Kentucky Derby and the Preakness.

His 20-year career was marked by great victories, questionable decisions, and emotional turmoil that led him into and out of four marriages and through a maze of different agents. After Johnny went to Chicago as an apprentice and lost his bug, his business fell off. He was having trouble getting mounts when he ran into Wayne Murty and asked Wayne to take his book—be his agent. Wayne took Johnny to Hot Springs, Arkansas, where business was slow at first, but gradually Wayne began to get Johnny back on some good mounts. Johnny won the Arkansas Derby on Count De Blanc in 1959 and ended up second leading rider.

Johnny fired Wayne shortly after the win in the Arkansas Derby and hired his father-in-law, Bill Lyons, to be his agent. In May of 1960, he fired Lyons and hired Bud Aime. In 1962, Sellers parted with Aime, and in the next two and a half years used at least four other agents.

In 1961, a smiling Johnny was on the cover of Sports Illustrated magazine. He was rubbing shoulders with the rich and famous, riding the best horses, and happily married to Janice Lyons. That same year, he won eight straight races, equaling an American record set in 1951. He ended the year as United States Champion Jockey by wins.

By 1963, he had been taken off Carry Back, and in May of that year he quit Wheatly Stables saying, "I just didn't get along with Mr. Fitzsimmons. He wanted me out at the barn at 6 a.m. I said I'd work any horse he wanted me to, but I didn't want to go out there just to hang around."

After making $180,000 in 1961 and another $120,000 in 1962, Johnny suddenly found himself scrambling to get good mounts.

"I got in with the wrong people," he was quoted as saying. "You get to be—you know, famous—and all these people are around. . . . Anyway, I seemed to lose my sense of values. . . ."

But Johnny's journey was far from over and he proved to himself and the world that he had the courage to make a comeback. In 1964, once again with the help of a fellow bush track rider. Wayne's brother, Duane Murty, became Johnny's agent. Johnny was quoted as saying, "Duane Murty is a good judge of horseflesh."

Johnny's observation of his friend Duane proved to be true. With Duane at the helm, Johnny equaled the world record for the mile in the Equipoise Handicap at Chicago while winning on Pia Star. In a span of four days, with Duane handling his book, Johnny won the Great American on Our Michael at Aqueduct, the Hollywood Oaks on Straight Deal at Hollywood Park, and the Brooklyn on Pia Star at Aqueduct.

In 1965, Johnny won the Belmont Stakes aboard Hail To All. In 1969, he was voted the George Woolf Memorial Jockey Award.

Throughout the 1960s and into the 1970s, Johnny continued his professional career. In 2007, he was inducted into the Hall of Fame in Saratoga Springs, New York. In 2011, he was inducted into the Racing Hall of Fame at Remington Park in Oklahoma City.

Johnny rode with both Eldon Nelson and Charlie Burr during his career. Sometime in the 1960s, after Eldon returned to the East Coast, he read an article about Johnny.

Realizing Johnny was from Oklahoma, he introduced himself as a fellow Okie. Eldon remembers riding against Johnny in a stakes race sometime after that, in which he took second and Johnny won. Eldon did not remember ever riding against Johnny after that, but said at one point he traded a registered bull for one of Johnny's saddle horses.

Charlie Burr rode with Johnny in the United Nations in 1961. Johnny rode Carry Back and Charlie rode Merry Ruler. The two also competed in the Don Handicap, Everglades Stakes, Boardwalk Handicap, Atlantic City Handicap, Benjamin Franklin Handicap, and the Ventnor Turf Handicap, all in 1961.

Many years after Charlie Burr's injury, in 1994, Johnny wrote a letter to Charlie and Mildred, inviting them to come meet him at Remington Park in Oklahoma City. Johnny promised to make everything wheelchair accessible and help Charlie any way he could. Because it was extremely hard for Charlie to leave his bed, the reunion never occurred.

Johnny retired in 1977 and moved to Hallandale, Florida, near Gulfstream Park racetrack. He enjoyed traveling overseas to places like Malaysia, where he acted as a horse broker, selling racehorses. Johnny has two sons, Mark, a former jockey, and John Michael, and a daughter, Sabrina.

Racing Wins

Washington Park Handicap (1958, 1960)
American Derby (1960)
Arlington Classic (1960)
Remsen Stakes (1960)
United Nations Handicap (1960)
Florida Derby (1961)
Jerome Handicap (1961)
Stars and Stripes Handicap (1961)
Alabama Stakes (1962)
Monmouth Oaks (1962)
Carter Handicap (1962)
Saratoga Special Stakes (1962)
Test Stakes (1962)
Whitney Handicap (1962)
Adirondack Stakes (1963)
Diana Handicap (1963)
Excelsior Breeder's Cup Handicap (1964)
Brooklyn Handicap (1965)

Ladies Handicap (1965)
Suburban Handicap (1965)
Travers Stakes (1965)
Kentucky Oaks (1967
Blue Grass Stakes (1967)
Hollywood Derby (1967)
Frank E. Kilroe Mile (1968, 1971)
San Gorgonio Handicap (1968)
Highlander Handicap (1969)
San Juan Capistrano Handicap (1969)
San Luis Obispo Handicap (1968, 1971)
San Pasqual Handicap (1968)
Del Mar Handicap (1970)
Strub Stakes (1971, 1973)
Del Mar Oaks (1972)
El Encino Stakes (1972)
San Felipe Stakes (1972)

American Classic Wins
Kentucky Derby (1961)
Preakness Stakes (1961)
Belmont Stakes (1965)

International Race Wins
Canadian International Stakes (1958)
Woodbine Oaks Stakes (1969)

Racing Awards
United States Champion Jockey by Wins (1961)
George Woolf Memorial Jockey Award (1969)

Honors
Remington Park Horse Racing Hall of Fame
United States' Racing Hall of Fame (2007)

Significant Horses
T.V. Lark, Carry Back, Hail To All, Cool Reception

Robert Nelson Ussery, 1935-_____

Bobby Ussery was born and raised in Vian, Oklahoma. He had no family influence when it came to horses or racing, but found himself at an early age astride Red, his grandfather Nelson Baker's mule. Bobby and his four brothers rode Red relentlessly whenever they had time. Crowding bareback on the sorrel mule, the boys had endless adventures in the Oklahoma hills.

A neighbor in Vian, Jack Phillips, spotted young Bobby one day and must have had the foresight to realize the small boy's potential as a jockey. Jack took Bobby under his wing and put him to work helping with his Quarter Horses. By the time Bobby turned 8, he was riding match races for Jack in Vian. One of Bobby's earliest memories is of Zeff Walters winning with Leo over Ponca Blue at 440 yards.

Coming from a large family in Oklahoma in the late '30s, Bobby had to learn to make his way in the world any way he could. With his slight build, no education and little support from his parents, riding horses soon become Bobby's bread and butter. So, at age 11, he left his family and moved to Oklahoma City with Otis Byron, who agreed to provide him room and board in exchange for riding horses.

At age 12, Bobby was completely on his own, riding the bush tracks at McLoud and Comanche, Oklahoma, and Del Rio, Fredericksburg, and Temple, Texas. By mucking stalls, cooling horses, galloping, and doing anything he was asked, the young bush track rider not only survived, but he slowly became engrossed in the life that would lead him to an unexpected destiny.

A year later, Bobby found himself living in Duncan, Oklahoma, working for Wade Johnson, who trained horses for Oscar Cox. He continued to work hard around the barns, listen, learn, and ride anytime the opportunity arose.

At 15 years old, Bobby traveled to Ak-Sar-Ben Race Track in Omaha, Nebraska, with Ed Reed of Fort Worth, Texas. Ed had Thoroughbreds, and by then Bobby had developed an interest in progressing from the rural Oklahoma bush tracks to the world of Thoroughbred racing. Upon his arrival at Ak-Sar-Ben, Bobby learned he had to be 16 years old to ride at a sanctioned track. He appeased himself by cleaning stalls, galloping horses, and gaining more knowledge.

Bobby's early journey led him from Ak-Sar-Ben to Centennial Race Track in Denver, Colorado, with Tommy Oliphant. In Colorado, he met R. D. Barns, a Western saddle maker who owned wild horses. From Colorado, Bobby traveled to Del Rio and went under contract to Dr. Johnson for $17.50 a week.

For awhile, Bobby was based in Sequin, Texas. One of his adventures during that time included flying out to Winslow, Arizona, to round up some wild horses.

In 1951, 16-year-old Bobby Ussery rode Reticule to victory in the Thanksgiving Handicap at Fair Grounds Race Course in New Orleans. The horse paid $28 to win. To any observer at the track that day, the win probably seemed inconsequential, but to the unknown, undersized boy from the rural bush tracks who had worked hard for five years to walk into that win circle, the race was a significant event. It was the beginning.

No one, including Bobby, would have believed back then that the young boy from Oklahoma would one day have a part of New York's Aqueduct racetrack named after him. "Ussery Alley" was named after Bobby rode his horse to victory over a dry strip of ground on an otherwise muddy track. And who could have imagined back in 1951 that Bobby would go on to ride 20,593 Thoroughbred horses, paving the way for his induction into the National Museum of Racing and Hall of Fame.

From the mid-1950s until 1974, Bobby dominated the New York and Florida racetracks, winning 17.5 percent of his races. He won the Preakness Stakes in 1960 on Bally Ache. He won the Kentucky Derby in 1967 on Proud Clarion and again in 1968 aboard Dancer's Image.

Unfortunately, after phenylbutazone, a substance banned at that time in Kentucky but later sanctioned after it was proven to not affect a horse's performance, was found in the post-race urine test of Dancer's Image, the stallion was listed as having finished last. But Bobby won the race. It was official. There was a payoff.

Today, Bobby says, "They should have left the numbers as they were and took the money away."

The doctor who treated Dancer's Image told Bobby after the race, "I don't know what happened."

Bobby, who was used to having to fight for his rights, kept the jockey's trophy for the 1968 "win." He would not return it to Churchill Downs. They had another trophy made for the rider of Forward Pass, who finished in second place.

"I have the trophy; it's mine," Bobby said. "I climbed aboard and I won."

The Oklahoma-born jockey had reason to be stubborn. He had nothing to do with any medication Dancer's Image had been given. When a jockey climbs on a horse, he trusts the owner and trainer to give him a clean mount. In the 136 times that the Derby has been run, Ussery's mount is the only one to be disqualified. At that time, Bobby would have been the fifth jockey in the history of Derby races to win the coveted prize back-to-back. To win the race and then be humiliated with the disqualification is an injustice that a jockey is not likely to forget.

Bobby remembers Wantha Davis from the Oklahoma and Texas bush tracks. He rode against Eldon Nelson in the Delaware Handicap in 1958. Eldon won that day on Endine. Bobby rode with Charlie Burr in the bushes, but Charlie was more advanced than Bobby when he began racing on the East Coast and in Florida. He knew Johnny Sellers. Johnny was the leading rider at Saratoga one year, when Bobby was leading rider at the other New York tracks. Bobby later met and became friends with the Murtys. Wayne Murty handled Bobby's book for a time, and the three old bush track riders remain friends today.

Bobby hung up his tack in 1974. Like any dedicated athlete, he hated to quit the sport he dearly loved. At that time, the money was getting better than it ever had been in his lifetime, but he felt an inner voice telling him it was time. He had fought his weight for years, the injuries and wear and tear of riding had begun to take its toll, and his motivation had begun to fade.

When Bobby retired, he was the fifth-leading money winner in the history of Thoroughbred racing. He was in the top 10 for wins six times, and top 10 for money earned nine times in his career.

Today, Bobby divides his time between Lexington, Kentucky, and his home in Hollywood, Florida. The Oklahoma boy who started match racing at 8 years of age remains an avid fan of the sport he dedicated his life to. Bobby has two children— Robert and Debbie.

Major Racing Wins

Canadian International Stakes (1955)
Manhattan Handicap (1957, 1967)
Sport Page Handicap (1957)
Whitney Handicap (1957)
Alabama Stakes (1958)
Cowdin Stakes (1958)
Travers Stakes (1958)
Jamaica Handicap (1959)
Toboggan Handicap (1959)
Flamingo Stakes (1960)
Florida Derby (1960)
Hopeful Stakes (1960)
Tremont Stakes (1960, 1961)
Black-Eyed Susan Stakes (1961)
Gotham Stakes (1961, 1965)
Fall Highweight Handicap (1961)
Mother Goose Stakes (1961)
Coaching Club American Oaks (1962)
Matron Stakes (1962, 1964)
Lawrence Realization Stakes (1963)
Brooklyn Handicap (1963, 1971)
Withers Stakes (1964, 1965)
Edgemere Handicap (1965)
Stuyvesant Handicap (1965)
Wood Memorial Stakes (1965, 1968)
Morris Handicap (1966)
Saratoga Special Stakes (1966)
Stymie Handicap (1966)
Carter Handicap (1969, 1970)
Comely Stakes (1959)

Canadian Classic Race Wins

Queen's Plate (1959)

American Classic Race Wins

Preakness Stakes (1960)
Kentucky Derby (1967, 1968)

Honors

United States Racing Hall of Fame (1980)
Oklahoma Racing Hall of Fame (2011)

Significant Horses

New Providence, Hail to Reason, Bally Ache, Proud Clarion, Dancer's Image

Charles Cloyd Smith, 1930-_____

Born in Daisy, Oklahoma, Charles "Charley" Smith was 15 years old when his family moved to a ranch in Kiowa, a rural community southeast of McAlester. Charley did not have an early desire to become a jockey, but he was in an area rich with running horses and racetracks.

Charley did become a horseman at age 6, when his father gave him a gelding named Knothead. Young Charley would hook his toes around Knothead's knee, jump, grab a handful of mane, and then used his bare feet to crawl up the horse's leg. Knothead had a bad habit of shying and dumping him on the ground, so the youngster's mounting technique quickly improved, and he learned to balance as he rode Knothead bareback through the rural Oklahoma hills.

Charley's father, Charles Griffin Smith, divided his time between managing a gro-

A pair of Kings–Charlie Smith, leading Quarter Horse jockey of his time and the mighty Jet Deck, World Champion of 1963, pictured in the Los Alamitos infield. Jet Deck was the first of his breed to earn over $200,000.

Charles Cloyd Smith on Jet Deck, 1936 world champion quarter horse, at Los Alamitos. Jet Deck was the first of his breed to win more than $200,000.

cery store and a herd of free-ranging cattle. Charley's mother, Alice Beulah Smith had a full-time job raising their three boys and five girls. Charley's older brother died in an accident in the early 1940s, and soon afterward, Charley, not yet a teenager, became his father's right-hand man.

Haying and gathering cattle didn't leave much time for an education or for pursuing dreams. Charley didn't compete as a jockey then, other than an occasional race between friends for fun. He remembers running one match race with three neighbor boys out in the pasture. It's doubtful that the seed to become a professional jockey was planted that day, because Charley took third place.

In 1948, right before he turned 18, Charley married Doris Jones. He quickly embraced the responsibility of making a good living for his coming family by taking a job in Oregon with an electric company. Later, Charley returned home and worked at a glass company, but carpentry work became his mainstay.

Gradually, a series of events changed the direction of Charley's life. About four years after his marriage, in 1952, Charley's father-in-law, Sam Jones, bought a horse out of the famous Painted Joe. Sam had been into match racing for years, and he immediately asked Charley to go out after work each day and gallop the horse. When it became apparent that Charley had the ability to sit a horse, others around the neighborhood began asking him to ride their horses.

The first few races Charley rode were simple match races in an Oklahoma pasture with no starting gates. The first official race he won was in Denver in 1957, at Centennial Race Track. Shortly after that win, Charley returned home to work at his full-time carpentry job, but the fever of racing and the thrill of being first across the wire were now in his blood.

Through the late 1950s and early 1960s, Charley rode on the bush tracks in Turley, Porter, and Newkirk, Oklahoma, on weekends while working his day job to support his family. He received between $1 and $5 for a ride. On a match race in Porter for Jessie Powell, Charley won on Pals Leo Sand. It was a $100 purse, and he received a $5 jockey mount. In the early 1960s, Charley won 30 of the 31 match races on the Oklahoma bush tracks.

Charley traveled with fellow bush track rider Harley Crosby to El Reno and rode a mare to victory for Floyd Jones. The $20 purse was a small fortune in the early 1950s. He also went with Harley to Missouri, to a weekend meet, and rode Thoroughbreds. They won every race they rode that day.

Sometime between 1957 and 1958, Charley rode a match race at Willy Hunt's father's place east of Tulsa, against a well-known woman rider named Wantha Davis.

Charlie Smith won the All American Quarter Horse Futurity in 1963 on Goetta.

Wantha and her husband had a little horse they matched against a horse owned by Charley's wife's uncle, Walter Jones. Charley outran Wantha by a neck on Leo Gan. Other bush track riders Charley knew included Harley Crosby, Gus McCarty, Gene Johnson, Tecumseh Starks, Don Allison, Willie Hunt, William Robertson, Shirley Barnes Hunt, Herman Moore, Jackie Myers, Cliff Lambert, Curt Perner, and Roy Brooks.

In 1958, Charley went to Florida to ride at Jacksonville and St. Augustine, where he was working his way up in the jockey standings, when he took a bad spill, broke his collarbone, and had to return to Oklahoma. By 1959, while still working as a carpenter, Charley returned to Denver, won 27 races, and became second-leading rider. His 45 wins that year ranked him second on the national scene.

Not long after the Denver success, a man named Harley Hanaford in Tulsa began coaching Charley, and soon talked him into taking some horses out to Bay Meadows in California. Charley's professional career as a jockey was about to launch. He won six races at Bay Meadows, then seven at Los Alamitos Race Course that summer, and 24 at the full meet, where he again was second-leading rider. Although Charley returned to work in Oklahoma after that, the news about his talent had traveled around the tracks.

By then, Charley began to entertain the possibility of making his living as a rider. He called a trainer named Lloyd Walker at Los Alamitos to see if Walker could use him. When Walker told Charley he had a place for him, Charley left his wife and two children in Oklahoma, packed up, and moved to California to see what he could accomplish as a full-time jockey.

By 1960, at age 30, Charley began to carve his place in jockey history. In the fall of 1961, he set a season record of 29 wins at Los Alamitos, and later achieved 78 victories that year, which made him the nation's top rider. He sent for his wife and children to join him. The Smith family would remain in California throughout Charley's celebrated career as a jockey. For the next decade, "Choo Choo Charley" became a well-known competitor.

Charley later rode world champion Pap, set records on Jet Deck, and won the All American Futurity with Goetta. Charley was leading rider of the nation for six years, and won 11 riding titles and more than 800 races in his career. In 1972, Charley officially retired as a jockey. The last race he ran was a match race in Mexico that he lost. Vessels Ranch later bought the horse named Beduino who outran Charley's mount, Chewarie, that day.

For the next 20 years, Charley served as head carpenter at Los Alamitos. He and his wife, Doris, remain in California today.

One day at the track at Los Alamitos, after Charley retired, he approached a young Oklahoma rider named G. R. Carter.

"Are you any kin to Barton Carter, over near Pawhuska?" he asked.

"That's my grandfather's brother," G.R. replied.

A look of remembrance shadowed Charley's face, along with a slow smile as he said, "I rode for Barton years ago, back in the bushes."

Charley Smith, dedicated husband for over 60 years, father of Michael Charles, Charla Jean, and Sherry Renay, and one of the most celebrated jockeys of his era, was inducted into the American Quarter Horse Hall of Fame in 2005. Charley was inducted into the Ruidoso Hall of Fame in 2007 and into the Racing Hall of Fame at Remington Park in Oklahoma City in 2010.

Duane and Wayne Murty, 1936-_____

Twins Duane and Wayne Murty were born in Guymon, Oklahoma, to Otis Anson and Theta Taylor Murty. The annual Pioneers Day Parade was held on May 2nd, which happened to be the twins' birthday, so every year from ages 1 through 3, they were proudly exhibited riding on the back of a wagon, wearing crisp new cowboy outfits. Perhaps it was that first experience as "cowboys" that instilled a love for horses in the twins that would last a lifetime.

In 1939, like so many Oklahoma families, the Murtys packed up and left their homestead which had become nothing but dust. Unlike many of the families leaving western Oklahoma after the Dust Bowl era, however, Otis, Theta, and their four sons traveled east to Tulsa instead of west to California. Duane and Wayne rode in the back of the truck with their pony, Tony, who entertained them during the long ride by eating their mother's new upholstered divan.

City life in Tulsa was less adventurous for the boys than had been life on the homestead, but because they were the only ones around with a pony, that they kept in the garage, they were soon selling horse rides to the neighborhood kids.

At around age 7, the twins began to spend a lot of time in the summer at their aunt and uncle's farm in Adair, Oklahoma. They learned to milk cows, ride mules, and work from a horse-drawn hay baler. One boy would ride the mule while the other wired and back wired.

At age 8 the twins began buying horses, breaking them, and reselling them for a profit. They were fortunate to have a mother who had few rules. She allowed them to buy the green horses, but told them, "Just let me get on them the first time."

Theta Murty had just about done it all in her lifetime. As a kid in Guymon, she had ridden her horse seven miles to school in every kind of weather. She constructed a doll museum and trading post, while occupying her spare moments writing poetry

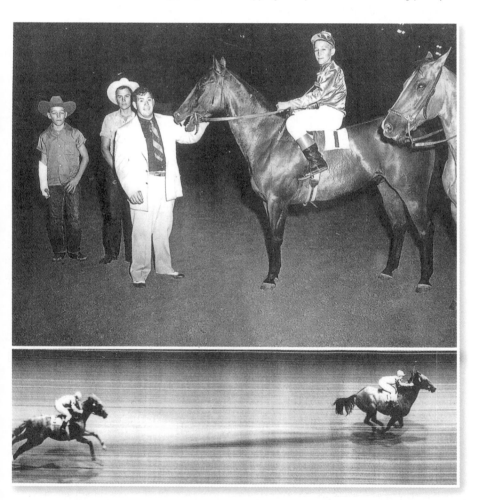

Duane Murty wins in Enid on F.L. King Bailey, owned by the Papan Brothers and trained by C.J. McCormick, outrunning Fairfax Leo. Standing on the far left with his arm in a cast from going through the rail in Cushing, Oklahoma, is twin brother, Wayne.

and catching rattlesnakes. She later drove stock cars and flew airplanes. She believed in letting her four boys have a loose rein.

When Wayne and Duane got into mischief and Theta cornered them, she always asked, "Okay, who did it?" The twins would point to each other. "Well, okay then," she would say, "Both of you will get punished."

At 12 years old, they were so experienced at riding that the parents of other neighborhood kids got together and tried to ban the Murty twins from entering the events at the summer rodeos. At one such competition, Wayne won eight of the events and Duane won the other.

Wayne Murty wins in Anthony, Kansas in 1952 on Old Jim, owned by P.F. Sale.

```
5R          MERCHANTS DERBY
1-Old Jim              2-Gold Star
3-Bronzaca      9F    T-2.2.0
PF Sale-owner         W Murty-up
WFTF     Anthony      7/25/52
                              FF
```

Very soon, the twins decided to try their luck at bull riding. Even though they were talented at the endeavor, the small bulls were able to turn with them in the chute and bruise the boys' chins badly. One day they had a "committee meeting" between the two of them and decided to go back to horses. They were tired of going around with bruised chins and banged-up legs.

Duane and Wayne were then fortunate enough to begin breaking horses for J.R. Cates, who had a great horse named Question Mark. They soon met Barton Carter, who took them under wing and began to teach them how to break and ride Quarter Horses and Thoroughbreds at the fairground in Tulsa.

The twins' early riding experience and yearning for adventure were the perfect match for the booming enterprise of the Oklahoma bush tracks. Soon they were traveling around the circuit, getting mounts at every meet. They shared one ball cap that they used for a helmet and one pair of worn boots.

For the next four years, they rode at Tulsa, Pond Creek, Ponca City, Pawhuska, Newkirk, Oklahoma City, McAlester, Wagoner, and anywhere else a meet was being held.

At 15, Wayne had an accident in Cushing while riding a moon-eyed horse. The horse went through an iron rail and rolled down an embankment. Wayne broke his arm in two places, had a concussion, and ended up in the hospital.

At 16 years of age, they ventured out of Oklahoma to ride in St. Louis, Missouri, and Columbus and Lincoln, Nebraska. Wayne was leading rider in Lincoln that year. They traveled on to California, where Wayne rode at both Los Alamitos and Bay Meadows.

In his riding career, Wayne won three races on a super filly named Loch Moeve. She was a Thoroughbred brought to the states from Germany by a soldier named Phil Sale. Hitler had ordered the papers on many horses to be destroyed, so the filly could never be registered.

During their short riding careers, the twins rode for Ben Johnson and Ben Johnson, Jr. Wayne galloped Miss Myers and Barbara L, two of the best mares in the country at that time. They both had a turn at riding F.L. King Bee, owned by the Papan Brothers in Ponca City and trained by C.J. McCormick. At Columbus, Nebraska, in 1953, Duane and Wayne ran a dead heat that ended up in Ripley's Believe It Or Not—Twins running a dead heat.

By age 17, the boys were getting too big to ride and were tired of the continuous battle to lose weight. They had another "committee meeting" and decided to retire as riders. But their journey and commitment to horse racing had just begun.

They not only knew most of the boys from the bushes, but they helped many of them find their way from the Oklahoma bush tracks to the Big Apple.

Today, in their mid-70s, Wayne and Duane live in Lexington, Kentucky, where they breed and race horses. They have a champion sprinting sire, Mister Phone, who is Argentine and American-bred.

George Robert Carter, Jr., 1968-_____

George Robert "G.R." Carter came from a family deeply rooted in horses and racing. His grandfather, Red Carter, was born in 1898 in Pawhuska, nine years before Oklahoma became a state. Red and his older brother, Barton Carter, took a special interest in breeding and training racehorses, and throughout their lives, the Carter brothers participated in and promoted horse racing in Oklahoma.

In a 1947 article from The Roundup, a picture shows a horse "owned and ridden" by Barton Carter taking second place. Barton was not a rider, but the picture proves that the Carter boys did whatever needed to be done to get their horses across the finish line. Red and Barton Carter, depicted today on a Native American mural on the Osage Nation Campus in Pawhuska, are two of only three Indians wearing cowboy hats.

Red and Barton seemed proud of their Osage Indian blood, and apparently the tribe respected the Carter brothers, who were only about one-sixteenth Osage. Barton Carter also is featured in the National Cowboy & Western Heritage Museum in Oklahoma City as a celebrated old-time cowboy.

It is no surprise that riding, match racing, and rodeo quickly became a way of life for G.R. Carter, born some 50 years after the Carter brothers began to carve their name on the wall of racing history. A win picture at Eureka Downs in Kansas in 1975 shows 7-year-old G. R. wearing a cowboy hat and boots, standing proudly in front of his parents. The winning horse, Cloud Runner, was owned by Holton H. Payne and Red Carter.

G.R. Carter, Sr. leaned more toward ranching and rodeo, so from the time he could walk, G.R. was schooled in the use of ropes and horses. At 4, he broke his arm from falling off of his horse, but he was back in the saddle before the cast came off. One typical afternoon, 12-year-old G.R. and his younger sister, Trona, were riding toward home from the fairgrounds. The two youngsters were riding on separate parallel roads when they spotted each other. Trona kicked her horse into a gallop and G.R. quickly took on the challenge by leaning forward and digging his heels into the flanks of his horse, Strawberry. Suddenly, Trona blasted by him on her big runaway gray horse, her eyes wide with terror. All G.R. could do was watch as his younger sister tried in vain to pull her mount toward the field, away from a dangerous cattle guard and fence that lay ahead.

G.R. Carter in a match race in 1983 in Alva, Oklahoma, riding # 3, Continental Robin, owned by Willie Carmen.

The horse refused to turn and blasted forward as Trona continued to fight for control. When the gray reached the cattle guard, he pivoted and dove over the fence gate with an unbelievable leap, only his back hooves clipping against the wood. When the horse jumped, Trona went over the saddle horn and was left clinging to the horse's neck, but somehow she quickly managed to maneuver her way back up into the saddle.

By the time the horse stopped, G.R. and Trona were both laughing so hard they had to dismount and sit on the ground to recuperate.

At 14, G.R. took his first summer job galloping horses at nearby Osage Downs in Pawhuska for a trainer named Gene Herren. A black jockey, Jerry Dailey, showed G.R. how to get a cross on the horse's reins that summer, and loaned him his helmet and all of his gear. G.R, Sr., along with Gene Herren, Bill Lau, and Leon Shaw, began to teach him how to get out of the gate, how to sit the horse, and all of the secrets to being a good rider.

G.R. in 1984 winning on Bea's Jester owned and trained by George Carter.

G.R. wins the All American Futurity in 1998 on Falling In Love Again, owned by David & Susan Mackie.

After G.R. had been galloping only about a month, he rode his first race in Claremore, Oklahoma, at the old fairgrounds on a mare named Continental Robin, owned by Willie Carmen and trained by Leon Shaw. He won his first purse of $20 that day. During that time, the standard pay was $15 to ride and $20 to win. G.R. walked away with his $20 and new confidence. This was not just a match race at Osage Downs in Pawhuska—he officially had won a real race against six other competitors.

During those early days, G.R. had to use all of Jerry Dailey's tack because he still did not even own a helmet. G.R. had a cowboy hat and a roping saddle, but nothing related to horse racing at that time. Before the summer was over, his parents bought him a helmet, which he secretly had longed to have. He did appreciate the use of Jerry's helmet, but G.R. was relieved to return the dirty, dented headgear and proudly strap on the shiny new one.

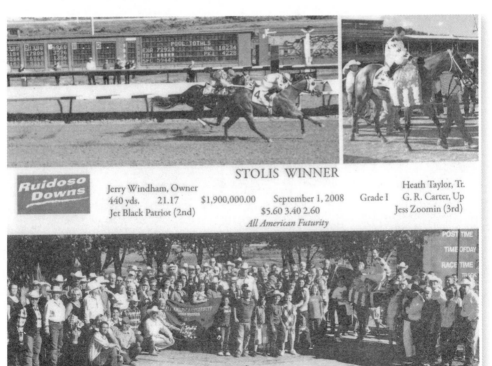

STOLIS WINNER

Ruidoso Downs

Jerry Windham, Owner
440 yds.   21.17 $1,900,000.00   September 1, 2008   Grade I
Jet Black Patriot (2nd) $5.60 3.40 2.60

Heath Taylor, Tr.
G. R. Carter, Up
Jess Zoomin (3rd)

All American Futurity

G.R. wins the 2008 All American Futurity on Stolis Winner, owned by Jerry Windham.

G.R., the Leading Man, on the cover of The American Quarter Horse Racing Journal.

By the time G.R. turned 16, his confidence as a rider had grown. He had ridden on the bush tracks in Alva, Claremore, Tahlequah, and Henryetta, and won approximately 50 races. During those bush track days, G.R. also rode in Stroud, Oklahoma, as well as Eureka and Anthony, Kansas. He met and rode with Harley Crosby, Floyd Campbell,

Herman Moore, and Tecumseh Stark's son, also known as Starkey. In 1984, G.R. won his first race on an official track, riding Bea's Jester to her maiden win at Blue Ribbon Downs in Sallisaw.

G.R. continued to ride on weekends at local bush tracks in Oklahoma, and rodeoed throughout his senior year of high school. By then, he knew he had the knowledge and athletic ability to do well as a jockey, but he had worked hard in school where he held a 4.0 grade average and would graduate as salutatorian of his class.

Even though his dream since childhood had been to earn a scholarship to Oklahoma State University, where his dad had graduated, and enter the school of veterinary medicine, when the second semester of his senior year arrived, the thought of eight more years of intense studying began to lose its appeal. He was torn between pursuing a career as a jockey or going on with his education. For weeks, G.R. wrestled with himself and his choices. He listened to well-meaning advice from family, counselors, and friends. Finally, he decided to throw his heart and soul into riding instead of college.

G.R.'s mother, Frankie, was disappointed with his decision, but his father stood by him. If George Robert Carter, Sr. had any disappointment over his son's decision to become a jockey, he never showed it. Instead, G.R.'s dad took him to Sallisaw, Oklahoma, after graduation in 1986, settled him in an apartment near the racetrack, and hung around for a few weeks to get his boy established.

Bill Hedge, the founder of Blue Ribbon Downs, happened to be an old friend of G.R.'s grandfather. Bill, a trainer, helped familiarize G.R. with the track and gave him the opportunity to ride some of his horses. Bill also introduced G.R. to Rex Brooks and Don Drake, other trainers that G.R. later rode for.

G.R. jumped into his chosen profession with an energy driven by a determination to succeed. He had made his choice, now he would give it his all. His background around horses and racing certainly gave him an advantage over the other young aspiring jockeys. The work ethic he had acquired helped too. G.R. had little time to look back. He galloped horses seven days a week and rode four or five days each week.

Another little known fact that probably contributed to G.R. Carter's early success was his experience as a high school wrestler. In 1986, as a 108-pound senior, G.R. won the state wrestling championship for PawhuskaHigh School. His dedication to wrestling not only taught him how to maintain his weight, but greatly enhanced his athletic ability.

G.R. won 17 races in 1986 after graduating high school. He won 57 in 1987 and 108 in 1988. By 1989, he won his first leading jockey title at Blue Ribbon Downs. He repeated that performance in 1990 at Blue Ribbon Downs, and won the overall title for American Quarter Horses, Paints, Appaloosas, and Thoroughbreds, beating Cliff Berry. He was leading rider at Fair Meadows in 1990, as well.

In 1990, four years after his start in Sallisaw, G.R. moved to Los Alamitos Race Course in Southern California. After three successful years in California, he moved his home base back to Oklahoma. Today, G.R. considers Remington Park in Oklahoma City his home, but he travels the country after the Remington season, and remains on top of his game as leading jockey of Quarter Horse racing.

G.R. met his wife, Shaena, through her brother, Mike Burgess. Mike and G.R. were friends and hung around together at the track in Sallisaw. G.R. looked up to Shaena's father, Jerry Burgess, who won the All American Futurity in 1975 riding Bugs Alive. G.R. and Shaena were married in 1992 and reside in Oklahoma City. The fact that Shaena grew up around the track and already knew the life and demands of horse racing made her the right partner for an aspiring jockey.

G.R. is proud to be the vice chair of the Jockey's Guild, and is passionate about the guild's purpose. He knows the history of those who came before him and appreciates the fact that what they went through made it easier for him as a rider. And although G.R. does not brag about his Native American heritage, he quickly points out that the two greatest Oklahomans "ever" were Will Rogers and Jim Thorpe.

The following incredible list of accolades is proof that then-18-year-old G.R. Carter made the right decision back in 1986, when he choose to pursue a career as a jockey. After pari-mutuel racing became legal in 1982, the bush tracks quickly shut down. G.R. Carter is the last jockey produced from that incredible era in Oklahoma history.

In 1982, when G.R. began riding, pari-mutuel racing was about to be approved in Oklahoma and the bush tracks were soon to be history. In 1984, G.R. rode in his first official pari-mutuel race at Blue Ribbon Downs. On that historic day, G.R. Carter, without knowing it, became the last of the boys from the bushes.

"Because of what those guys went through, things were easier for me." —G.R. Carter, December 29, 2009

Racing Wins (As of 2009)
All American Derby (1972)
All American Futurity (1998, 2008)
All American Gold Cup (1995
Bank of America Challenge Championship (2000)
Bayer Legend Derby Challenge Championship (1977, 2005)

Black/Gold Futurity (2002)
Blue Ribbon Derby (1995, 1998)
Blue Ribbon Futurity (1997, 2007)
Championship at Sunland Park (2005)
Dash for Cash Derby (1997, 2006, 2007)
Ed Burke Million Futurity (2006)
Ford Juvenile Challenge Championship (1995)
Go Man Go Handicap (2006)
Golden State Futurity (2002, 2003)
Governor's Cup Futurity (2006)
Governor's Cup Derby (2007)
Harrah's Entertainment Derby (2006)
Heritage Place Derby (1989, 1998, 2004, 2007)
Heritage Place Futurity (1988, 1989, 1994, 1997, 2002)
Hobbs American Futurity (2009)
Kansas Derby (2007)
Kansas Futurity (2007)
Kansas Jackpot Derby (2005)
Kansas Jackpot Futurity (2005, 2009)
Kindergarten Futurity (1993)
Lazy E Derby (1996)
Los Alamitos Invitational Championship (1998)
Los Alamitos Super Derby (2003, 2004)
Los Alamitos Two Million Futurity (2002, 2005)
Los Alamitos Winter Derby (2004)
Mildred Vessels Memorial Handicap (1993, 2003)
Mile High Derby (2002)
Oklahoma Derby (1989, 2007, 2009)
Oklahoma Futurity (1992)
Oklahoma Horsemen's Association Derby (2000, 2003)
Oklahoma Horsemen's Association Futurity (2004)
PCQHA Breeder's Futurity (2004)
PCQHA Breeder's Derby (2009)
Rainbow Derby (1998)
Rainbow Futurity (1996)

Red Cell Distance Challenge Championship (1996, 2003)
Refrigerator Handicap (2006)
Remington Park Derby (1998, 2004, 2007)
Remington Park Futurity (1997, 2001, 2007, 2009)
Remington Park Invitational Championship (2007)
Ruidoso Futurity (2004)
Sooner State Stakes (1996, 2001, 2005, 2006, 2007, 2008)
Southern California Derby (1995)
Speedhorse Gold & Silver Cup Derby (2002, 2005)
Speedhorse Gold & Silver Cup Futurity (2002, 2008)
Spencer Childers California Breeders Championship (2004, 2005, 2006)
Sunland Park Winter Derby (2003, 2004, 2007)
Sunland Park Winter Futurity (2005)
Texas Classic Derby (1997, 2006, 2009)
Texas Classic Futurity (2006)
Vessels Maturity (2005, 2006)
West Texas Futurity (2008)
West Texas Maturity (2007)
Zia Derby (1997, 2004)

Racing Awards
AQHA World Championship Jockey (1993, 1997, 2003, 2004, 2005, 2006, 2007, 2008)
APHA World Championship Jockey (1997, 1998, 2000, 2002, 2004, 2005, 2007)

Honors
Racing Hall of Fame at Remington Park in Oklahoma City
Ruidoso Downs Race Horse Hall of Fame
May 31, 2009—G.R. Carter Day was declared by Governor Brad Henry in Oklahoma

Significant Horses
Be A Bono, Country Chicks Man, Dashin Is Easy, Dashing Perfection, Fallin In Loveagain, Fast First Prize, Fast Prize Zoom, FDD Dynasty, Hez Ramblin Man, Got Country Grip, Jess Zoomin, Noblesse Six, PYC Paint Your Wagon, Stolis Winner, Valiant Hero

THE END OF AN ERA

The demise of rural horse racing on unsanctioned bush tracks meant the end of an era. The American jockey is slowly becoming extinct as riders from South America, Mexico, and other countries where bush tracks still exist are now in the forefront. Today, a young man in this country must be 16 to get a license to work on a recognized racetrack.

By the time an Oklahoma bush track boy turned 16 and went to ride on a sanctioned track, he had ridden hundreds of horses and worked endless hours around the barns. He had developed the skill to get a horse out of the gate, learned to stay astride equines that were half-broke, often crazed with drugs, shocked with machines, and sometimes beaten into submission. When the rural American bush tracks shut down, the door of the "Bush Track School" closed, greatly reducing and perhaps forever ending America's ability to produce qualified jockeys.

In the name of progress and, arguably, the name of child welfare, the days of the bush tracks and the bush track boys are now history.

A classic photo by Gene Wilson Associates taken of the Bush Track Jockey Colony in Pond Creek, Oklahoma, in 1946-1947.

BIBLIOGRAPHY

INTERVIEWS

Allison, Don Grant
Brock, Lewis Albert
Brooks, Roy
Burr, Charles E.
Campbell, Floyd
Carter, George Robert, Jr.
Chase, Barbara Ann Berry
Church, Joyce
Crosby, Harley Eugene
Davis, Wantha Lorena
Epperson, E. Clayton
Gladd, Janet
Grizzard, Johnny
Hartley, Ida
Herber, Lucille
Hunt, Shirley
Hunt, William
Martin, Virginia
Moore, Herman
Murty, Duane
Murty, Wayne
Nelson, G. Eldon
Perner, Curtis William
Sellers, Nita
Smith, Charles Cloyd
Stark, Tecumseh
Stone, Calvin
Thomas, Joe
Ussery, Robert Nelson
Wells, Oscar, Jr.

MAGAZINES/PERIODICALS

Blood Horse, The
Chronicles of Oklahoma, The
Monmouth Park Bugle
Quarter Racing Record, The
Speedhorse
TIME Magazine

NEWSPAPERS

Arkansas City Traveler
Arlington Notebook
Baltimore Sun, The
Chicago American, The
Conway Springs Star
Courier Journal
Kansas City Star, The
Kansas City Times, The
Miami Daily News
Miami Herald
Monmouth Park Bugle
Native American Times
New York Herald Tribune
Philadelphia Inquirer, The
Ponca City News
Quarter Racing Record, The
Roundup, The
Sentinel-Record, The
Speedhorse
Sunday Oklahoman, The
Trinidad Chronicle News
Tulsa World